Best of
Historical
Tales

TINY TOT PUBLICATIONS
INDIA

Best of
Historical Tales

Written by:

Zakir Ali 'Rajneesh'

Edited by:

Shyam Dua

Published By:

TINY TOT PUBLICATIONS

235, Jagriti Enclave,
Vikas Marg,
Delhi-110092 (INDIA)
Ph.: 2216 7314, 2216 3582,
Fax:- 91-11-22143023
email: tinytotpub@hotmail.com

ISBN : 81-304-0312-9

Illustrated by
Rustagi. P. R.

CONTENTS

FOR THE SAKE OF HONOUR

It was evening time. The sky was clear and the breeze was giving a cooling affect. The prince of Hada clan, Kumbha was walking on the road that connected the jungle to the city. On his left shoulder he was carrying his bow and arrow and on the right, a big bag was hanging. He seemed to be very tired.

Suddenly he stopped when he looked at something near the village. His eyesight had caught the construction work of a fort that was going on. The structure of the fort resembled the fort of Bundi. Seeing this, Kumbha was shocked. 'The fort of Bundi on the land of Chittor! What could be the reason behind this?' With this thought in mind Kumbha reached the fort. He asked a man who was giving instructions to the labourers, "Brother, why the fort of Bundi is being constructed in Chittor?"

"To fulfill the promise of Maharana," was the reply.

"What was the promise of Maharana and to whom that prompted you to construct the fort of Bundi on the land of Chittor?" Kumbha asked the man, who was actually the officer-in-charge.

The officer looked at Kumbha carefully. Then he narrated the reason for the construction of the fort.

Chittor and Bundi were two different kingdoms. Bundi was a very small kingdom in comparison to Chittor. Once it was ruled by Chittor. But the Rajputs living there didn't like to be ruled by someone else. Gradually, they increased their power and declared Bundi a separate kingdom. Maharana of Chittor strongly objected to this. He attacked Bundi but was defeated in the battle. The disappointed army returned to Chittor.

Time passed by, but Chittor could never forget the humiliation it had suffered at the hands of Bundi. Maharana increased his military

power to many times. He was very keen to avenge the defeat. One day Maharana of Chittor sent a letter to the king of Bundi which read, "Accept our rule or Bundi would be destroyed."

Hama, the ruler of Bundi, when received this

message, got seriously disturbed, but he decided to handle the matter with patience. He sent a strong reply of the letter that read, "We are not at all frightened by such fake threats. Bundi is our motherland and we have won it by our strength. We will not let you capture Bundi. If you have courage then face us in the battlefield."

With this reply, Maharana of Chittor got furious. He asked his army to get ready for the war. Soon, the army of Chittor marched towards Bundi. The fort of Bundi was located on a hilly region. The road to the fort was very rough and uneven. The army took a lot of time to reach the fort. When it reached there, it was badly tired and not in a condition to face the war. The soldiers camped outside the fort to rest there. Maharana and the army chief discussed about the war for a long time. They were quite confident that they will win the war.

By that time, Hama also had a good preparation for the war. When he came to know that the army of Chittor was taking rest just outside the fort, he decided to attack the enemy at that very moment. Taking a force of mere 500 soldiers, he launched the attack. The tired army of Chittor was not at all ready for the war. Soon they got surrounded from all the four sides. They tried their best but could not face the Rajputs. Again Maharana had to face the defeat.

Maharana felt very upset on this defeat. The most remorseful reason was that he lost the war at the hands of mere 500 soldiers. This imposed a black spot on his name and fame. What will one say on hearing the news? Thinking about all this, Maharana became more upset and sad. The fire of

revenge was burning in his heart. He wanted to win Bundi at any cost.

The next day, when Maharana reached the court, he saw the shameful faces of his courtiers. The brave warriors of Chittor didn't have the courage to raise their eyes. There was complete silence in the court for a long time. Everyone was thinking that who will start the proceedings of the court?

Maharana could not bear the pain for a long time. He at last broke his silence and said, "We have lost the battle against a troop of 500 soldiers only. This is very shameful for us. The fame of Chittor has turned to dust. It is useless to live such a disgraceful life, but still we have to live. We have to avenge our defeat."

No one uttered even a single word. Maharana continued, "It is our first responsibility to safeguard the honour of Chittor. And for this reason, I am taking a vow, I will not eat anything till I defeat Bundi."

All the courtiers were stunned to hear this. It was not an easy task to win the fort of Bundi. For that, many preparations were needed. It could take many years. If Maharana will not eat anything then.."

At this, one of the ministers spoke up, "*Maharaj*, please take back your words. It is not so easy to win Bundi."

"Yes *Maharaj*, we will try our best to win Bundi as soon as possible," said the army chief, "but please

take back your words."

"Yes *Maharaj*, please take back your words," repeated all the courtiers to support the army chief. But Maharana didn't deter from his vow. The courtiers tried a lot to make him understand, but seeing that Maharana would not listen to them, they started thinking of some other solution.

After some time, one courtier said, "Maharana, there is a way. If you permit me, I can tell it to you."

On getting the permission, the courtier said, "Let us make a fake court of Bundi here in our kingdom. The soldiers could also live in there. Then you can win it and have food. We will keep on with the preparations. Then we can attack Bundi and win it. In this way, you can keep your vow and we can win over Bundi also."

Maharana at first didn't like the idea, but when the courtiers compelled him, he had to agree. Thus, the construction work of the fort of Bundi started in Chittor.

Some families of the Hada Rajputs of Bundi lived in

Chittor. They were actually once arrested by the soldiers of Chittor, but after their release, they decided to settle down in Chittor. Kumbha was the leader of those Hada Rajputs. When he came to know about the whole matter, he got very angry. How dare Maharana insult his motherland for the sake of his vow?

Kumbha hurriedly returned to his village. He gathered all the Hada Rajputs and narrated them the entire story. The Rajputs could not control their anger on hearing this. They immediately took

their weapons and marched towards the fake fort to protect the honour of their motherland.

Next morning, Maharana reached the fake fort of Bundi with his army. As soon as the elephant on which Maharana was sitting reached near the fort, many arrows came flying by and got buried all around the elephant. Maharana surprisingly asked the army chief, "What is all this?"

The army chief got frightened. He went near the fort where he saw Kumbha with his men. Kumbha said to the army chief, "The leader of Hada Rajputs welcomes you at the fort of Bundi."

"How dare you raise your weapons against Maharana?" roared the army chief.

"We have been forced to pick up our weapons. We cannot tolerate such an insult of our motherland," replied Kumbha.

"But don't forget that you have been living in Chittor for such a long time," said the army chief.

"I can sacrifice my life for Maharana. But as far as this fort is concerned, its security is my first responsibility. Moreover, I don't want people to say that Maharana just won the fake fort of Bundi. He is a coward. For this reason, I am giving this fake fort a real touch," said Kumbha.

"Shut up, you will get punished for this," said the

army chief.

"We do not care for our lives. If I had to lay down my life for the sake of my motherland, I would be the happiest

person in this world," said Kumbha.

"OK, now get ready to face the consequences," said the army chief and went away.

After a while, the whole army of Chittor attacked the fake fort of Bundi. Kumbha and his men fought bravely in this war, but because they were few in number they soon got martyred. In this way, the Maharana of Chittor won the fake fort of Bundi.

Seeing the bravery of Kumbha and his men, Maharana was stunned. He gave up the idea of conquering Bundi. Kumbha's sacrifice worked for his motherland. Bundi was never threatened again or had to face a war against Chittor.

THE BRAIN POWER

The court of Rajput king Juja was set. In the centre of the court, a big piece of betel leaf was kept on a dish. One who would eat that betel leaf would have accepted the challenge of suppressing the rebellion in the northern region. The king had announced that whosoever will succeed in this work would be given the reward of his choice. All the famous warriors of the kingdom had tried their level best but to no avail.

In the court, Juja's nephew Devraaj was also present. He was going through a bit of rough patch at the moment. His father Vijayraj had been killed by the king of Bhatinda. Devraaj and his mother had somehow saved themselves from the cruel hands of the king of Bhatinda. Since then, they had been living in the palace of Juja. Devraaj wanted to gather strength so that he could avenge his father's murder.

"Is there no one in the court who dares to accept the challenge?" asked Juja and looked at every courtier. All the courtiers bent their eyes in shame. Devraaj felt that it was the right opportunity to win the confidence and reward of Juja.

Thinking this, Devraaj stood up and went to the table. He picked up the betel leaf and ate it. Now there were many courtiers in the court of Juja who were jealous of Devraaj. They felt very happy thinking that they would get rid of their enemy.

Devraaj took a troop of 1000 soldiers and marched towards the northern region to cut the heads of the rebels. With their bravery and courage, Devraaj and his soldiers killed many of the rebels. Those who survived either fled away or surrendered themselves. Devraaj reached the court of Juja with

the surrendered rebels.

The news that Devraaj had won the battle had already reached the ears of Juja. He stepped down from his throne and embraced Devraaj, "I am proud that I am the uncle of such a brave and courageous Rajput. I give you my heartiest congratulations on this win. Tell me what reward do you want?"

Devraaj replied, "*Mamaji*, all this was possible due to your blessings. Let me first go and meet my mother. She must be worried. After that I will take my reward."

After getting the permission, Devraaj went to meet his mother. On seeing Devraaj, his mother embraced him and blessed him, "Long live, my son. Now I have firm belief that you will bring back your father's lost honour."

On the other side, the courtiers of Juja were filling his ears against Devraaj, "*Maharaj*, make sure that Devraaj doesn't ask for something that might cause danger to you."

"Yes *Maharaj*, a person who is capable of winning a battle against those furious rebels, can do anything," said another courtier.

In reality, Juja was a very weak-minded and a suspicious person. He felt as if the courtiers were right. He thought, 'I should better be careful with Devraaj.' Devraaj after meeting with his mother returned back to Juja.

Asking for his reward Devraaj said, "*Maharaj*, as a reward I want the vacant land located in the south."

Juja felt suspicious. He asked, "Devraaj, that piece of land is barren and rocky. Why do you want it?"

Devraaj already knew the nature of his uncle. He spoke up, "*Maharaj*, you had announced that whosoever would succeed in suppressing the rebellion in the northern region would be given a reward of his choice. Then why this question?"

"Devraaj, you know that the land in the southern region is very important from political point of view. Therefore, you have to tell me the reason," said Juja.

"But *Maharaj*, this will break the rule of the betel leaf," said Devraaj with anger. "At that time, you didn't put any such condition. Moreover, Rajputs are famous for fulfilling their promise even at the cost of their lives."

"Don't teach me the principles of Rajputs, Devraaj," Juja also got angry. "Don't forget that you are under my guardianship. So be in your limit."

Devraaj felt to separate the head of Juja from his torso. But anger could deteriorate the situation. So, he stood up and went to his mother.

On knowing about the behaviour of Juja, Devraaj's mother was shocked. In the evening, when Juja was taking rest in his chamber, she went there and made him understand the things.

When Juja's anger calmed down, he said, "OK, I will give that land to Devraaj."

The next day, Juja, Devraaj and all the courtiers reached the land which Devraaj had asked for. After looking at the land carefully, Juja said, "OK Devraaj, you will be given only that much land as the length of the skin of a buffalo."

On hearing this, Devraaj got enraged. But he remembered his mother's words, "Son, you should always try to deal with the situation using your brain. Physical strength doesn't work at every place."

"*Maharaj*, do you promise that I will be given land as much as the skin of a buffalo? asked Devraaj."

"Yes," was the reply. Then Juja signalled and a man walked there with a skin of buffalo. He spread the buffalo skin and started measuring the land.

Just then Devraaj said, "Wait, first you cut this skin into minute pieces and make a rope out

of them."

"But what for?" asked Juja.

"Just wait and watch *Maharaj*," said Devraaj.

The man got busy in his work. After some time, a long rope got ready of the skin of the buffalo. Taking the rope, Devraaj started making an enclosure. A few kilometres of land came under that enclosure.

After that, Devraaj came to Juja and said, "*Maharaj*, I need only this much piece of land."

Juja got trapped in his own trick. He said to Devraaj, "OK, I give you this piece of land."

On getting the land, Devraaj became very happy. He made a fort on that land. Due to its huge size and architecture, the fort became very famous. Even today, the fort narrates the story of bravery and intelligence of Devraaj.

THE UNKNOWN GUEST

It was winter season. The sun had set a little bit earlier than the usual time. Cool breeze was blowing which was making the weather colder. No one could be seen on the streets of Agra. At this time, a man was walking down the street humming a song. He was walking on that lonely street in such a way as if the Emperor of Hindustan was roaming in his palace.

Behind that man another man was coming. He had covered himself with a big blanket. After some time, the man who was walking in the front felt the presence of the other. He turned back. The man in the blanket had reached very near to him. He bowed his head and said very humbly, "*Huzoor*, why have you stopped singing? Your voice is very nice. Moreover, your choice of ghazals is very good."

"Thank you," said the man walking in front, with a

smile on his face. "Did you really like the ghazal? Actually this is my own composition."

"Very good! Great!" admired the man in blanket. "Your ghazal is really very nice. By which name do you compose your ghazals?"

"Sir, my name is Sikander," the man replied.

"You really write and sing very well. By your name I can presume that one day you will become a famous poet," said the man in blanket.

"This is your modesty. I am just a simple poet, who composes poems as a hobby," said Sikander and took out a small box from his pocket. Forwarding the box to that man, he said, "Please take a *paan*."

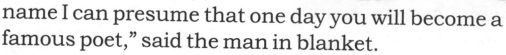

"Oh, you seem to be a poet in totality," said the man in blanket putting a piece of *paan* in his mouth. "Sikander *saheb*, aren't you afraid of walking in this lonely street?"

"Sir, I don't have anything to be afraid of. One who is very wealthy is always fearful. I have only the blessings of *Allah* and nothing else. Moreover, our Emperor Jehangir is a very responsible ruler. He

rules so well that no offence occurs in the kingdom."

"Yes, you are absolutely right," the other man said. "Sikander *miyan*, your *paan* was nice just like your composition."

"In such a case, please come to this poor man's house tomorrow. Whatever is there in my house, we friends will share it. I will also sing some of my best compositions to you."

"But what about my *paan*?" asked the man.

"Sir, *paan* will surely be there. Don't worry," said Sikander and laughed out loudly.

"So don't forget my feast tomorrow," said the man and shook hands with Sikander. "But Sikander *bhai*, you didn't tell me your address."

"Oh, I forgot to tell it. I live in the village of weavers near the next crossroads. My house is just at the entrance of the village. And yes, there is a palm tree in front of my house. It is a landmark."

"It's OK then. Moreover, you are such a good poet. Anyone can guide me to your house," said the man and went on his way.

Sikander turned towards his house thinking about the man in blanket. Suddenly, he remembered that he had forgotten to ask that man about his identity. Who was that man? From where had he come from? These questions made him restless. He turned around, but couldn't see the man.

'Whoever he may be, he was a gentleman. He was very fond of listening to ghazals. He praised my ghazal so much. When I will tell about this to my wife, she will not believe it,' thought Sikander and moved fast.

Next morning, Sikander got busy with the preparations to welcome his new friend. He cleaned the whole house. Then he went to his field and brought some legumes. He asked his wife to cook a delicious meal for his friend. Sikander's wife was surprised when she saw him roaming outside the house waiting for his friend. She said, "You are getting so excited, as if the person visiting us is none other than the Emperor himself."

"Is there anything special about the Emperor? A person is liked by his behaviour and not by his status," said Sikander to his wife. "My friend is no less than Emperor Jahangir. He is a great man."

Sikander's wife made faces and got busy with her work. As the sun set, beatings of drums came from began to be heard in the village of weavers. The villagers were surprised to hear the sound of royal drums. People came out of their houses to see what the matter was. They were shocked to see Emperor Jahangir approaching on his elephant.

Sikander also saw the Emperor. He felt as if the face of the emperor resembled the face of the man he had met the previous night. 'So, was that man.......?'

Sikander was thinking all this when the Emperor with his men reached his house. Jahangir alighted from the elephant. He looked at Sikander and said, "Friend, would you not call me inside?"

Sikander came out of his dreams. He bowed before the Emperor and took him inside the house. The condition of the house was very bad. Jahangir sat down on the cot that was spread there. He said to Sikander, "Friend, please bring the food. I am very hungry."

Sikander brought the food his wife had prepared and served it to the Emperor hesitatingly. After finishing the food quickly, Jahangir said, "After a long time I have eaten such a delicious meal."

After that, Jahangir ate a *paan* and listened to some ghazals of Sikander. At the time of leaving, he said to Sikander, "You didn't know about me, still you invited me and gave me such a warm hospitality. I am very happy. Take this small gift from my side." And gave a bag to Sikander.

Before Sikander could understand anything, Jahangir had stepped out of his house. He hurried away to bade his friend goodbye. Jahangir said, "I like your *paan* and ghazals. I will come again."

Then the royal cavalcade went off. To Sikander it was just like a dream. When he opened the bag given by Jahangir, his eyes glowed to see gold coins inside it.

The king of Malwa, Yashodharman's court was all set. Many neighbouring kings were gathered there to discuss a serious matter. They wanted everyone to get united and face the Hunos. Hunos had come to India from the Middle Asia and created a havoc in the country. When they saw that small kingdoms were always engaged in fighting with each other, they attacked them and thus, won many kingdoms of India.

Baffled by such a situation, all the kings of small kingdoms had gathered in the court of Yashodharman to decide how to deal with the matter. They proposed to attack the Hunos with combined strength.

Just then, a soldier came in and after bowing to the king he said, "Maharaj, one Huno soldier wants to meet you."

"Huno soldier!" Yashodharman was shocked. "OK,

send him in."

The next moment, a Huno soldier entered the court. After greeting the king, he said, "*Maharaj*, I have brought a message for you sent by your sister Mallika. She is at present imprisoned in the prison of the Huno ruler. She has sent her ring as a mark of recognition."

At first, Yashodharman couldn't recollect about whom that Huno soldier was talking about. But when he saw the ring, he recalled an old incident.

At that time, Yashodharman was a prince. He was very fond of hunting and going to various places. He would often go for hunting expeditions with his friends and would return home after many days. His parents were always worried due to his long absence. They always would try to make Yashodharman understand but he took no heed of them.

One day, Yashodharman was on a hunting expedition with some of his friends. Suddenly, his eyes fell on a deer. He aimed at

it and shot an arrow. But the deer was quick. It jumped aside and ran away. Yashodharman started chasing the deer. The deer reached the dense forest and suddenly got disappeared. Till then Yashodharman had got separated from his friends. He was very sad regarding the deer. At the same time, he felt thirsty. Just then, he heard the noise of a flowing river. He went

that way. At a short distance there was a river. Yashodharman jumped from his horse and went towards the river to drink water. As he was drinking water, he lost his balance and fell into the river. The flow of the river was very fast. The prince tried to swim across the river but couldn't do so. He started flowing with the water.

Flowing by, the prince passed by a village. A girl was filling water in her pitcher at the riverside. When she saw the prince flowing by, she jumped into the river and saved him. Then the girl made Yashodharman lie on his back and took out all the water from his body. The prince came back to his senses.

Yashodharman sat up and stared at the face of the girl. The girl was extremely beautiful. Yashodharman looked at her and said humbly, "I am thankful to you for saving my life. I am Yashodharman the prince of Malwa. Even if I give you my entire kingdom, I won't be able to repay your kindness."

"This was my responsibility which I fulfilled," said the girl. "I didn't do it to earn any reward, therefore I don't expect anything."

Hearing the words of the girl, Yashodharman got impressed with her. He said, "You seem to be of a high class family. What is your name? Will you marry me?"

The girl got serious at this. She said, "My name is Mallika. I am a brahmin whereas you are a Kshatriya. Therefore, I can't marry you. Please forgive me. But I would want you to become my brother, if you want."

"Why not?" said

Yashodharman. "I will be happy to have an intelligent and courageous sister like you."

Then Yashodharman gave his ring to Mallika and said, "Keep this ring with you as a memento of your brother. Whenever you need any help, just remember me. I will help you at any cost."

Mallika took the ring. She smiled at Yashodharman and returned back home taking her pitcher. Yashodharman kept looking at her till she vanished from his sight.

Today when Yashodharman saw his ring, he remembered his sister. He said, "This ring belongs to my sister Mallika who once saved me from drowning when I was a prince. Where is she right now? How is she? And from where did you get this ring?"

The Huno soldier at first got confused of having so many

questions at a time. But then he started narrating everything from the beginning.

Soon after this incident, Mallika got married. As time passed by, she gave birth to two children. The life of Mallika kept running smoothly. Her children had now grown up. Once, the Huno ruler Mihirgul attacked Mathura. Mallika got arrested with her family.

Mihirgul agreed to set her and her husband free on the condition that her son will join the Huno army and her daughter will marry a Huno soldier. But Mallika refused to accept the condition. Mihirgul got angry at this. He gave orders to imprison Mallika and her family and they were not to be given food to eat or water to drink.

Mallika and her family were dying when she met a kind soldier in the prison. That soldier would bring fruits for Mallika and her family. Mallika was spending her life in a hell. Then she remembered her brother Yashodharman. She requested the soldier to take her message to Yashodharman. At first, the soldier didn't agree but after continuos pleadings, he consented.

On learning about the condition of his sister, Yashodharman became very angry. He gave some presents to the soldier and bade him goodbye. Then he, along with all the other kings, prepared a strategy to face the Hunos in a war.

Yashodharman with a large army attacked the Hunos. A fierce battle was fought between the two. Yashodharman's army defeated the army of Mihirgul

and the latter's soldiers fled from the battlefield.

After defeating Mihirgul, Yashodharman went to Mathura to liberate his sister and her family from the prison. He was very eager to see his sister. But when he reached the prison where Mallika and her family were imprisoned, he came to know that she had already died. On seeing her dead body, Yashodharman could not hold his tears and started crying bitterly.

Yashodharman was very much affected by his sister's death. He pledged to drive the Hunos out of the country. He again gathered the whole army and attacked the Hunos. Yashodharman and his army kept fighting till they drove the Hunos out of India.

THE HUT AND THE TEMPLE

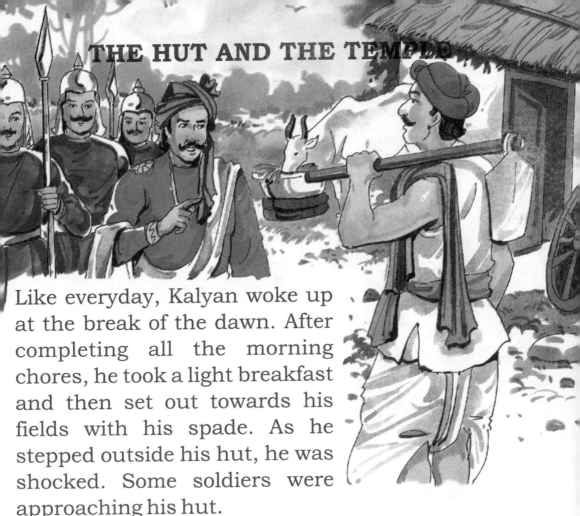

Like everyday, Kalyan woke up at the break of the dawn. After completing all the morning chores, he took a light breakfast and then set out towards his fields with his spade. As he stepped outside his hut, he was shocked. Some soldiers were approaching his hut.

'What are these soldiers doing here at this hour of the day?' thought Kalyan. 'Hope the neighbouring kingdom has not attacked us.' There were four men in total. Three of them were soldiers and the fourth one looked like a minister. The minister came forward and asked, "Is your name Kalyan?"

"Yes, what is the matter?" asked Kalyan.

"You have to vacate your house," ordered the minister. "The king wants to build a Shiv temple in the middle of this kingdom. The royal architects have chosen this place for the temple."

"But this is my land," said Kalyan. By then Kalyan's

wife also came outside. Kalyan scolded her, "Go inside! Can't you see I am talking?"

After she went inside, Kalyan said to the minister, "This is our ancestral property. Our...."

The minister had not got enough time to listen to the reasoning of Kalyan. He said, "This is the order of the king. You would be given two times more land as compensation. If you don't vacate your house till tomorrow evening, your hut would be broken down."

Then the minister and the soldiers went away. Kalyan kept standing at his place. He felt as if someone had snatched away everything from him. His wife came outside and some neighbours also gathered there.

"The king has got so much of land. Still he wants to build the temple by breaking the huts of poor villagers," one neighbour commented.

"But we have to obey his orders at any cost," said another man.

"I will not give away my land," shouted Kalyan. "This is our ancestral property. I will give up my life but not this land."

Kalyan's wife consoled him and took him inside. Then she tried to calm him down, "OK, we will not give our land. We will appeal against the king. How the king can snatch our land?"

Kalyan talked to his neighbours but none of them dared to support him. But Kalyan didn't lose hope. He went to the court. He kept his case in front of the judge. After listening to the whole case, the judge made the decision, "A king is the owner of all the things in a kingdom. We use his things with his permission. But if he wants to take something back, we can't refuse him. Moreover, you are getting two times of your land as compensation."

Hearing the decision of the judge, Kalyan felt disappointed. He understood that he would have to lose his land. Next day, in the evening, the minister again arrived at Kalyan's house. This time the number of soldiers was twenty. Seeing him, Kalyan started shouting, "I will not give my land, I will not give my land!"

The minister signalled the soldiers and they started breaking the hut of Kalyan. The minister ordered them, "Be quick! The work should be completed before the sunset. Tomorrow morning the king will perform *puja* here."

After that, the minister went away from there. The soldiers got busy with their work. Soon, the hut of Kalyan turned into a heap of rubble. It was night. In the middle of the sky the moon was glowing brightly. The king of Kashmir Chandrapeer was getting ready for the bed after having his dinner. Just then someone rang the plaintiff bell. The king was shocked. 'Who rang the plaintiff bell at this hour of the day?' he thought.

He ordered a soldier, "Bring the plaintiff."

The next moment, the soldier entered the chamber with a man. The king saw that the man's clothes were stained with mud. His hair was not properly combed and on the cheeks the stain of the tears was clearly visible.

The king asked him, "Who are you? What is your problem?"

"My name is Kalyan," said the plaintiff. "And you are responsible for such a condition of mine."

The king was shocked, "Me! But I am meeting you for the first time."

"But it was your order to construct a temple at the middle of the kingdom," said Kalyan. "For this reason, the minister broke my house. My belongings

are scattered around. I went to the court, but there also I didn't get justice. Now I have come to you with hope."

'But the minister didn't tell me that there is a hut at that place,' thought the king. He then summoned the minister. When the minister saw Kalyan, he understood everything. The king asked the minister angrily, "You broke the house of this man for the construction of the temple?"

"*Maharaj*, you told me that the temple should be built at the centre of the kingdom. The architects told me that the place near Kalyan's hut is the appropriate place," said the minister.

"And so you left Kalyan homeless," shouted the king. "I am surprised that the judge also didn't listen to the pleas of Kalyan. Now go and reconstruct the hut of Kalyan. I will think about the temple later."

Kalyan was happy on hearing the decision of the king. He praised the king and went away from there. The minister immediately reached Kalyan's land with some labourers. He ordered the labourers to rebuild the hut. Soon, the hut was ready. The minister sought forgiveness from Kalyan and left the place.

Next morning, when Kalyan woke up, he heard the sound of the royal drums. He stepped outside his house and saw that the king was approaching his hut. By then his wife had also come outside. She too was surprised. The neighbours also gathered there. They were shouting, "Long live the king!"

The king alighted from the elephant and went to Kalyan. Kalyan and his wife bowed before the king. The king said to Kalyan, "Kalyan as you know there is only one Shiv temple in this kingdom and that too is located on the outskirts of the kingdom which is very far from here. People had to suffer many problems in reaching there. For this reason, I have taken a pledge to build a Shiv temple in the centre of this kingdom. As per schedule, the *puja* of the land was to be conducted today. But due to the ignorance

of the minister, the programme had to be postponed and you also faced many problems."

Kalyan wanted to say something but he was tongue-tied. The king continued, "Since I have taken a pledge, I want to build the temple right here in the centre of the kingdom. Therefore, I ask you to give me this piece of land as an alm. Please give me this land which is also your ancestral property for the construction of the temple. I will be highly obliged to you."

Hearing this, Kalyan said, "*Maharaj*, please don't make me feel guilty. All the things I possess are your properties. Please construct the Shiva temple on this piece of land. My ancestors will also feel very happy on knowing that their land is being used for the construction of Shiva temple."

On hearing the conversation between Kalyan and King Chandrapeer, everyone was surprised. After that, *puja* was performed and the construction work started. As compensation the king gave a huge mansion to Kalyan. Kalyan started living in the mansion happily with his family.

SHREWD VYASKAR

Ajaatshatru became the king of Magadh after killing his father Bimbasaar. He was a very clever and powerful ruler. Very soon he increased the size of his kingdom. Everywhere people were talking about him. The people of Magadh had forgotten Bimbasaar and were praising Ajaatshatru.

One day, the court of Ajaatshatru was in session. He was discussing about the extension of his borders with his ministers. One minister said, "*Maharaj*, today, you are the main topic of conversation among the people. There is no king who can look into your eyes."

"Yes Lord," said the second minister. "This is only because of your valour. You have strengthened Magadh on the map of India."

Hearing his ministers, Ajaatshatru smiled and said, "I know all this, but there is still one work left which needs to be done."

"Which work, *Maharaj*?" asked several ministers together.

"Winning Vaishali!" said Ajaatshatru.

Hearing Ajaatshatru, all the ministers became silent. Vaishali was a very strong kingdom. The people of Vaishali were known as Lichivi. There was no categorisation of king and subjects in Vaishali. It was a democratic kingdom. The people of Vaishali themselves chose their leader. The leader considered himself as the servant of the people and with heart and soul looked after the kingdom. If anyone looked at it, they would teach him a good lesson. For this reason, Vaishali was still a republic country.

The soil of Vaishali was very fertile. There were many rivers and streams in the kingdom. Apart from these, there were big parks and gardens. The production of crops was very high. For all these reasons, the people were very happy.

Ajaatshatru was well aware of about the bravery and strength of Lichivis. Because of this, he had still not dared to attack this kingdom. In the court of Ajaatshatru, there was a shrewd minister named Vyaskar. He knew about the king's intention. He said, "*Maharaj*, I want to say something in this context."

Ajaatshatru looked at Vyaskar who was smiling softly. Ajaatshatru was well aware of the shrewdness of Vyaskar. He asked him, "What do you want to say?"

Vyaskar whispered something in the ears of the king. Hearing his plan, Ajaatshatru got excited. He said to him, "Vyaskar, I did not expect this from you." He called the army chief angrily.

The whole court was surprised . What did Vyaskar say to the king that he got so much angry? The army chief took out his sword and said, "What is the order, *Maharaj*?"

"Kill Vyaskar," roared the king.

"Please forgive me, *Maharaj*," pleaded Vyaskar. "I will go away from this kingdom, but please pardon me."

The Prime Minister also pleaded for Vyaskar, "*Maharaj*, he has been serving you for so long. Please forgive him."

"Yes *Maharaj*, please forgive him," prayed all the courtiers.

"OK, as all of you are requesting, I take back my order of death sentence, but I don't want to see his face again. Paint his face black and throw him out of the kingdom sitting on a donkey."

The army chief obeyed the king's order. He painted Vyaskar's face black and threw him out of the kingdom. Insulted, Vyaskar reached the bank of river Ganga and washed his face in the water. He then swam across Ganga and reached Vaishali.

Vyaskar immediately went to the leader of Vaishali. Narrating his sad story, Vyaskar said, "Sir, this way Ajaatshatru rewarded me for serving him so many years of my life. He threw me out of his kingdom. Now I am at your refuge."

The leader of Vaishali was already aware of all the happenings through his spies. He said to Vyaskar, "Every person living in Vaishali have equal rights. You can stay here peacefully."

Hearing this, Vyaskar fell at the feet of the leader. The leader made him stand and gave him a small task. Vyaskar completed the task with full perfection. In a few days, Vyaskar became a popular figure in Vaishali. The leader got pleased with him and made him the chief judge.

As per his nature, slowly Vyaskar started removing the robe of an honest and dutiful person. He started instigating people against each other. He had a unique way of doing this task. First, he would invite an important person for a feast with him. Then after gaining his faith, he would instigate him against some other important person.

Slowly, Vyaskar through his evil means polluted the whole Vaishali. The people now became shrewd, cunning and selfish. They were now enemies of each other. They would search new ways to earn money. Thus, the whole kingdom deteriorated.

One day, a function was held in Vaishali. Vyaskar served all the people of the kingdom with wine at his expense. Now every person in the kingdom the leader, soldiers and the general public — were in a state of intoxication. Seeing this, Vyaskar felt very

pleased. Till now all of his moves had proved right. The motive behind his coming to Vaishali seemed to be on the path of success. Vyaskar rode his horse and went to the gate of the city. The soldiers were lying senseless there after drinking wine. Vyaskar opened the gate. Outside, Ajaatshatru was ready with his army. As soon as the gate was opened, the army entered into Vaishali.

When the soldiers of Vaishali saw this, they drew out their swords. But what could they have done in the state of intoxication? People who were earlier always ready for a battle were now hiding themselves inside their houses. Soon, Ajaatshatru took control of Vaishali in his own hands.

Because of shrewd and clever Vyaskar, Ajaatshatru conquered Vaishali. The Lichivis became the slaves of Ajaatshatru. In this way, the only republic ended forever.

THE RIGHT DECISION

It was an inauspicious evening in the history of India. The lion of Mysore, Tipu Sultan was walking in his chamber rather uneasily. The reason was the defeat in the third war of Mysore. His own trusted men betrayed him in this war. As a result, a major part of Mysore went to the British.

Just then, an attendant came inside and informed Tipu Sultan, "Sir, British Governor General Cornwallis's messenger wants to meet you."

"Send him in," said Tipu.

Soon, a British officer came inside. After saluting the king, he told him the motive of his coming, "The Governor of Bengal, Lord Cornwallis has sent the documents of treaty. After reading them....."

Just then, Tipu's teacher and guardian, Pandit Purniya came in. Tipu moved forward and greeted him. Understanding the intention of Tipu, Purniya took the letter in his hand and asked the messenger to leave. After saluting both of them, the messenger went away.

"Please read it," said Tipu taking a deep breath. "Let me see what General Cornwallis has written in the treaty."

"OK," said Purniya and started reading the letter.

"Mr. Tipu Sultan, everyone is aware of the fact that East India Company has always helped the Kings and Nawabs of India. In return of our help, they provide us with one thing or the other. The company wants peace and prosperity to spread in the whole country, so that people can live in peace and good frame of mind. But there are some Indian rulers who always want the opposite. They hate us because of no reason. To make them quiet, the company has no option but to use the force."

"Very well said," said Tipu with a humorous smile.

Purniya looked at Tipu and continued with the

letter, "The Battle of Mysore in which your army had to face the defeat, is a lesson for you not to repeat your mistake again in future. Now the company wants a peace treaty with you for which you have to follow three conditions of ours. In such a case, you will remain the king of Mysore or else...."

"You just read out the three conditions," interrupted Tipu.

"OK," said Purniya and started reading the conditions. "The first condition is to compensate the loss which the company has suffered due to the battle, which is three crore thirty lakh rupees. Second condition is that you will never try to fight 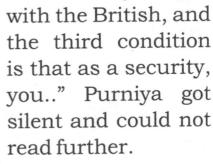 with the British, and the third condition is that as a security, you.." Purniya got silent and could not read further.

"What happened Panditji?" asked Tipu. "Let me see how much torture the British wants to enforce upon us."

"You have to send your two sons as security to Cornwallis..," said

Purniya.

"Cornwallis!" shouted Tipu and his face went red with anger. His hand went to his sword. Seeing the reaction of the king, Purniya also got scared. Then he controlled himself and said, "Your Majesty, please don't accept this condition. In this way......"

"What can we do if our own people betray us? We don't have any option left right now other than to accept the conditions," there was sadness in Tipu's tone. "We can't let our remaining soldiers die."

"That is all right, but sending the princes to the British would mean giving prey to a hungry fox. Like this, we will completely become slaves of the British. We will have to do as they would want us to."

Tipu remained silent. Purniya continued, "Sultan, why don't we send some other children in the guise of the princes?" "How is this possible?" asked Tipu. "First of all, they would be recognised, and secondly, my heart will not accept this thing."

"But Sultan, we need to see the security of Mysore and the freedom struggle, not our respect or fame.

The two princes are not only your sons, but also the future of Mysore. If something happens to them then what will be the future of Mysore?"

"You are right Panditji, but..." Tipu was still confused. "As I love my children, in the same way.... Who will agree to send their children to those Britishers? And if somebody agreed then also..."

"Sultan, we cannot face the situation being emotional," said Purniya. "We need to take some hard decisions. The two princes are your sons, but in the first place they are the future of Mysore. Sultan, we cannot let you do so."

"OK, let me think for a while about the matter. Only then I would be able to take any decision," said Tipu.

Purniya went away from there. Tipu thought for a long time. Suddenly, there arose a pain in his heart as the faces of his sons floated in front of his eyes.

'Because of the battle, I couldn't meet my sons for such a long time,' thought Tipu and set off to meet his sons.

The two sons were waiting eagerly for their father in their room. Tipu's eldest son, Khaliq, was 10 years old. He was very fond of listening to the war stories of his father. His younger son, Mujaauddin, who was 8 years felt very relaxed in the lap of his father.

On seeing their father, the two princes ran to him and embraced him. When Tipu saw smile on his sons' faces, he felt very relaxed. Taking them in his arms, he started pampering them.

"*Abbu jaan*, I have a complain against you," said Khaliq in a stern voice.

"Me too," shouted Mujaauddin.

"O, you both have complaints against me," said Tipu pretending to be in a state of shock. "Let me know what I have done to my loved ones."

"We have heard that according to the peace treaty, you are sending some other children in place of us," said Khaliq.

Hearing Khaliq, Tipu was surprised. He asked him, "But how did you come to know about this?"

"We secretly heard the conversation between you and Purniya Pandit," came the reply. Tipu took a deep breath. To change the topic, he said, "But sons, it is wrong to hear conversations secretly."

"For that we are very sorry," said Khaliq holding the hands of his father. "But *abbu jaan*, this is not right that someone else should be sent to the Britishers in place of us."

Tipu became quiet. Khaliq continued, "This is indeed wrong and unjust. We will not allow this to happen."

"Yes *abbu jaan*, what if we are small, we will go to the Britishers," said Mujaauddin.

"O my loved ones," said Tipu and hugged his sons. Tears came into his eyes.

"*Abbu jaan*, this is an examination for us. If we get afraid at this time then what will everyone say?

Only that Tipu Sultan sacrificed two innocent children to the Britishers for the sake of his fatherhood," said Khaliq like a matured person.

Tipu looked at Khaliq in amazement.

Khaliq continued, "*Abbu jaan*, we can lay down our lives happily for your name and fame, but we will not let you do a thing which is wrong. Moreover, we have full faith in you. We know that within a short span you will free us from the British captivity."

"OK, my sons. It will happen just as you want. For the sake of my fatherhood, I will not take advantage of my status and sacrifice two innocent children," said Tipu and stood from his seat. Now he had no confusion in his mind. He looked at his sons and set off for announcing his decision to Purniya.

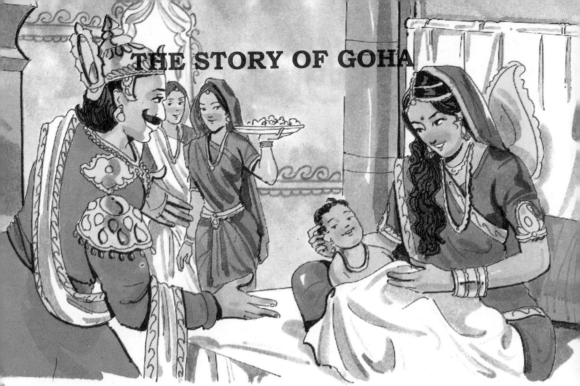

THE STORY OF GOHA

Shiladitya was a brave and clever man. He was the king of Saurashtra. He had declared Vallabhi as the capital city of Saurashtra. Shiladitya was counted among the famous kings of the Sun dynasty. Shiladitya was a strong man of principles. He could not tolerate injustice and tyranny. He never forgave any criminal. He gave severe punishments to the people who would break the law of the land. For these reasons, there was peace and happiness in the kingdom.

Pushpawati was the wife of Shiladitya. She was a very beautiful and brave woman. After many years of worship, she gave birth to a boy. On getting the news of the birth of his son, Shiladitya was very happy. He distributed clothes and money to the poor and needy as charity. The whole kingdom was decorated. Seeing the munificent nature of their king, the subjects felt very pleased.

Now, because of the stern nature of Shiladitya, some of his ministers were not in his favour. They got united with Tataro, the enemy kingdom. They revealed all the important secrets of Saurashtra to the Tataro king Tatar. Tatar was looking for such an opportunity. He attacked Vallabhi. At that time, celebrations were going on in Vallabhi at the birth of the prince. As the Tataros attacked the kingdom, there was panic everywhere. Shiladitya faced the enemy with his full might, but couldn't deal with the well-prepared Tataros. Shiladitya died fighting the battle.

When Pushpawati came to know about it, she fled away with her new-born child through a tunnel accompanied by a trusted maid. They reached a jungle where they took shelter in a temple. Tataros

searched for the queen and the child everywhere, but to no avail.

The temple in which Pushpawati had taken shelter, was located at the border of the jungle. The people of the village often used to visit the temple. This was a cause of concern for Pushpawati. Therefore, she hid in the caves at some distance from there. Once, Pushpawati suffered from fever. The maid named Kamla got tensed. The village was far from there and if she went there for any help, she might get caught.

Before Kamla could do something, the condition of Pushpawati worsened. One day, Pushawati breathed her last. Now Kamla had a big responsibility on her shoulders. She had to look after the prince. She took the baby in her lap and set off towards her village Beernagar.

Kamla's parents were pleased

on seeing her. She had returned to her home after several years. When her parents asked about the child, she told them that he was her son. The innocent parents trusted her. So, the heir of the Sun dynasty started spending his childhood in the house of a brahmin woman. Kamla named the prince as Goha. Goha was just like his father, brave and just. As Goha grew up, he started going to various places with the children of the village. One day, he met some tribal children. Seeing their bows and arrows, he got attracted towards them. He became friendly with those tribal children and started learning archery.

Slowly, Goha became an expert archer. Living with those tribals, he also learnt swordsmanship and wrestling. Seeing Goha's bravery and intelligence, the tribal children got impressed with him and chose him as their leader.

One day, Goha had gone to the jungle with those tribals for hunting. Suddenly, a boar attacked the tribals. It wounded two of them which resulted in bleeding. Seeing this, Goha got angry. Taking his knife, he pounced on the boar.

The boar attacked with its sharp paws. But Goha got aside and saved himself. The boar got furious on seeing its attack go in vain. It again attacked Goha. This time Goha was fully prepared. Just as the boar reached near him, he stabbed the knife in its stomach. Goha sat on the boar and stabbed it repeatedly. Soon, the boar breathed its last.

Seeing the dead boar, Goha's friends became very happy. They picked Goha on their shoulders and praised him. Just then, a boy said, "Let's present this boar to our chieftain Mandlik. He will be very happy on seeing such a big boar."

"Yes, he will reward us," said another boy.

Goha had no objection to this. He himself wanted to meet Mandlik for many days. He picked up the boar and they all set off to meet the leader.

It was a festival time for the tribals. There was a festive mood in the court of Mandlik. A dancer was dancing when Goha reached there with his friends. They decided to wait for the dance to end.

Suddenly, Mandlik's eyes fell on the boar lying near Goha. He got surprised. Such a big boar! A boar of similar size had attacked Mandlik two days ago. He had somehow saved himself. Mandlik thought, 'It this the same boar?'

He ordered the dance to be stopped

and asked, "Who killed this boar?"

"Me," said Goha coming forward, and bowed down his

head in front of Mandlik. Mandlik looked at the boy with amazement. He shouted, "Don't try to befool me. In my kingdom, anyone who tries to cheat gets the death sentence."

"*Sardar*, he is telling the truth," said one of Goha's friends. "He killed the boar in front of us."

"Very good, very good," said Mandlik and came to Goha. He then looked at the boar carefully. After recognising it, he said, "It is the same boar that attacked me two days ago. How did you kill it?"

"By this knife," replied Goha.

Mandlik was amazed to see the confidence of little Goha. He asked, "Who are you and where do you live?"

"I am a brahmin. My name is Goha and I live in

Beernagar," replied Goha.

"Brahmin? It's impossible," exclaimed Mandlik and came nearer to Goha. He stared at him and asked him again, "Tell me the truth, who are you? A brahmin cannot do such a brave task."

"I am telling you the truth. My mother's name is Kamla Devi. We are brahmins," said Goha strongly.

Mandlik looked at Goha carefully. Round face, sturdy body and confident voice. He thought that the boy must be a *kshatriya*. But why did he say that he was a brahmin?

Suddenly, Mandlik's eyes fell on the locket that Goha was wearing. Such lockets were being wore by princes and kings. He asked, "What about this locket?"

"This is a memento of my late father," replied Goha.

"What happened to your father? Let me see the locket," saying so, Mandlik moved towards Goha.

"No, you can't touch this locket. My mother has instructed me not to let anyone touch this locket," saying so, Goha clutched the locket in his hand.

Mandlik reached to Goha and snatched the locket. He opened the locket and saw King Shiladitya's stamp on it. On seeing the stamp, Mandlik jumped with joy, "This is the stamp of our late king, Shiladitya. So you're his son."

The next moment, Mandlik kissed the hands of Goha. He said, "You are alive, the son of the great king Shiladitya. I am very happy. I was thinking that the Tataros had killed everyone present in the palace."

Mandlik asked Goha to sit on the throne. He addressed all the tribals, "He is our king Shiladitya's son. Let's all celebrate this moment."

When Kamla came to know about this, she felt very happy. She went to Mandlik and told him the truth. Mandlik helped Goha in every possible way. Gradually, Goha grew up and assembled a big army. And on the basis of it, he laid the base of the Gehlot dynasty.

THE JUSTICE OF QAZI

It was evening time. The birds were returning to their nests and the animals were coming back to their resting places. Tired of whole day's work, the people were in a hurry to reach their homes.

Qazi Shamsuddin also returned to his house after a busy day in the court. Reaching home, he first washed his face and then wiped it with a clean towel. Then he sat down on a cot. His servant brought him a glass of water. The qazi drank water and was about to lay down on the cot when he heard a woman crying loudly. He understood that there must be a plaintiff outside.

The qazi stepped out of his house. When he saw the scene outside, he was stunned. An old woman was carrying her son who must be about twelve years old. An arrow was pierced in his back. There were blood stains all over the clothes of the boy.

"Have pity on me!" said the old woman and made her son lay down on the ground.

"What happened to him?" asked the qazi looking at the arrow. "Who shot the arrow at him?"

"Sir, my son had gone to the jungle to cut wood," said the old woman crying. "There the sultan shot him with an arrow. Sir, he was my only hope. Now who will look after me?"

On hearing the name of the sultan, the qazi got a shock. The woman was talking about Sultan Gayasuddin Balban, the Emperor of Pathan dynasty. The complain was against him. Now what could be done? He thought for some time and then asked, "Do you have any proof that the arrow belongs to the sultan?"

"Yes sir," cried the old woman. "Two children of the village had also gone with my son to the jungle. They saw the sultan with their own eyes. But sir, they are very frightened and are refusing to give witness. Now you are my last hope. Please have pity on me."

"Don't worry, you will have justice," the qazi consoled the old woman. Then he became thoughtful. 'If there was no one to give witness then how could it be proved that the sultan had shot the.....' Suddenly, the qazi's eyes fell on the arrow that was pierced in the boy's back. He took out the arrow and saw the royal stamp on it.

"OK, you come to the court tomorrow morning. You will have justice," said the qazi and kept the arrow with him.

Hearing this, the old woman heaved a sigh of relief. She returned to her home taking her son's body with her. The qazi had solved many difficult cases in his life. But this case was related with the sultan. He kept the arrow in the cupboard and started thinking about how to deal with the case.

Next day, the whole court was crowded. Everyone wanted to know what punishment the sultan would get. At the scheduled time, the qazi reached the court and sat on his seat. The old woman and the sultan were already present in the court. The qazi had summoned them.

The qazi showed the arrow to the sultan and asked him, "This woman has complained against you that you have killed her only

son. For this reason, you have been summoned to the court. Do you have anything to say regarding this?"

The sultan took the arrow and observed it carefully. Indeed there was the royal stamp on the arrow. He said, "I accept my fault. But I didn't do it intentionally. I shot the arrow aiming at a deer. The aim was not perfect and the arrow hit this woman's son. I am prepared to accept whatever punishment you decide for me."

"On the basis of the proof and the acceptance of guilt by the sultan, I have reached the conclusion that the sultan is guilty," said the qazi. "I give order to the sultan to seek forgiveness from this mother. He should also perform the last rituals of the boy in the royal manner. I also order him to give a thousand

gold coins as penalty to this old woman, so that she could look after herself in this old age."

"I accept the punishment," said the sultan. "But if you had practised partiality thinking that I am the sultan of this kingdom, I would have killed you." Saying this, the sultan took out a sword that he had brought hidden in his clothes.

Hearing this, Qazi Shamsuddin also stood up from his place and took out a whip from his clothes. He said, "Sultan, I was also ready. If you had refused to obey my orders, I would have whipped you badly."

On listening this, the sultan felt very pleased and embraced the qazi. He sought forgiveness from the old woman and gave her one thousand gold coins as compensation. On getting the money, the old woman felt a bit relieved. She then thanked both the qazi and the sultan and returned home.

THE DEATH SENTENCE

It was spring season. There were some clouds in the sky. A cool breeze was blowing. The three daughters of King Fatehsingh of Mewar were having fun on the swing. Kesar the youngest daughter loved to swing with her sisters.

The two elder daughters of the king were already married. They had come to their father's house for some days. The two sisters were telling interesting stories about their in-laws to Kesar. Kesar was enjoying the company of her sisters when Kamla, the maid came to her and said, "Princess, please grant me a leave for today."

"Leave!" Kesar stared at her. "But why?"

"Princess, do you remember Ramrati? Her husband has died. That's why.....," said Kamla bowing his head.

"Who is Ramrati?" Kesar stopped swinging. "The one who works in the kitchen?"

"Yes princess."

"Oh! What happened to her husband? She had got married just some days ago!" exclaimed Kesar.

"Actually, the king gave him death sentence."

"Death sentence!" Kesar was shocked.

"Kesar, what happened to you? Let's swing," said one of her sisters.

"No *didi*, I don't want to swing anymore. Please let me rest. I am not feeling well," said Kesar.

"Princess, should I bring water for you?" asked Kamla.

"Yes, please bring some water for me," Kesar said.

Kesar alighted from the swing and sat down at a place. Kamla brought water for her. After drinking water, Kesar felt slightly relieved. She then asked Kamla, "Now tell me, what happened to Ramrati's husband? Why did Maharana give him death sentence?"

Kamla sat down on the grass in front of Kesar and said, "Her husband used to feed the horses in the

stable of Maharana. Few days ago fifteen horses died mysteriously and he was accused for their death."

"But what is his fault in this? It may be due to the neglect of the keeper of the stable," said Kesar.

"Princess, no one heeds the poor. Everyone proved him guity and a liar," said Kamla.

"I think Ramrati would be very sad," Kesar said showing her concern. "How many children she has?"

"She has two daughters. One is three years old and the second one is just born. Ramrati is behaving like a lunatic. I am very worried about her little children," replied Kamla.

Kesar didn't say anything. Kamla asked her, "Princess, can I leave now? There is no one to look after her. I can atleast look after her kids."

Kesar gave her the permission. She was feeling very sad. She went to her room and laid down on her bed. She was thinking about Ramrati. She recalled what had happened just two days ago. Ramrati had

cooked *halwa* and *puye* for lunch. Kesar loved to eat *halwa* and *puye*, especially if cooked by Ramrati.

That day Kesar was eating her favourite dish with relish when Maharana scolded Ramrati, "If you dare prepare these dishes ever again then you will be dismissed. Kesar is gaining weight day by day."

"*Bapu*," resented Kesar, "If you ever say anything to Ramrati, I will not eat anything."

"Oh dear, I was just kidding. I know that you love to eat dishes made by Ramrati."

That day, Kesar didn't take her lunch and dinner. Whenever food was kept in front of her, she thought about Ramrati. During night, she could not sleep properly. When she woke up in the morning, she was burning with fever. The royal physician was called at once. He gave Kesar some medicines. After taking medicines for two days, Kesar got well.

After the death of her husband, Ramrati had become mad. She was unable to think about anything. Whole day, she would say only one thing, "He hadn't done anything." Kamla felt pity on her and adopted her children.

Kesar was very upset to learn all this. She did not like the idea of death sentence. What if some horses of the stable had died? It doesn't mean that you can give death sentence to any person. It is against humanity. A happy family had been ruined due to such a rule. One death sentence took the lives of the whole family. Death sentence should be banned.

After some days, Kesar's marriage was fixed with the king of Jodhpur. There was festive mood in the whole kingdom. But Kesar was not at all happy. She was still thinking about poor Ramrati. At the scheduled time, the bridegroom party reached the palace. All the rituals were performed, and the subjects gave presents to their dear Kesar.

Soon, Kesar's departure time came. She was going to be parted with her father today. Kesar started crying bitterly. Maharana blessed her and asked,

"Why are you crying dear? You are going to your in-laws."

Kesar hugged her father. As she was about to sit in the palanquin, she said, "Father, can I ask you for one thing?"

"Sure Kesar," said Maharana.

"But promise me first that whatever I will ask you for, you will give it to me," said Kesar.

All the people present there were surprised. Maharana said, "Kesar, I promise you. Now tell me what do you want?"

"The death sentence," replied Kesar.

"What?" exclaimed Maharana. "Death sentence!"

"Yes father, I want that from today, no one in Mewar should be given death sentence," Kesar said. Maharana understood what Kesar wanted to say. He said, "As you wish dear. No one in Mewar would ever be given the death sentence."

Kesar was happy and her face brightened. All the people present there shouted with joy. Everyone praised Kesar. Kesar went to her in-laws with her husband. Since then death sentence was never given in Maharana's entire tenure.

THE REWARD

The kingdom of Tikamgarh was located in the impassable mountains of Rajasthan. That day there was a festive mood in the whole Tikamgarh. The soldiers were rewarded for their allegiance and bravery. In the end, the turn of King Mahendra Singh's nephew Nagendra Singh came. Looking at him, Mahendra Singh said, "You are like my son. You showed valour and bravery in the battle with the British that lasted for four years. It is my duty now to reward you. Tell me what do you want."

Nagendra Singh stood up from his seat and went to King Mahendra Singh. Touching his feet, he said, "*Maharaj*, it was my duty. As far as the reward is concerned, I just need your blessings."

Mahendra Singh was very pleased. He said, "My blessings are always with you. But still I want to reward you at this auspicious moment. What do you want?"

"*Maharaj*, in such a case I want two rewards," said Nagendra Singh with a smile on his lips. "But I can't ask for my rewards openly. I will tell you only in secret."

"It seems that you want some special reward," said the king laughingly. "You can ask for your rewards anytime you wish. You have my promise."

Hearing this, all the courtiers were shocked. Everybody was thinking what reward Nagendra Singh would ask for? With that, the king ended the day for the court.

"Nagendra, what kind of reward do you want from the king that you couldn't ask in the court?" asked Gajendra Singh, Nagendra's father and the army chief of Tikamgarh. "I hope your intentions are good."

At this, Nagendra replied, "Father, no one had ever raised his finger at the intentions of Rajputs."

After some time, Nagendra went to the king. Seeing him, the king said,

"Come Nagendra, I was just thinking about you. Now tell me what do you want as your rewards."

After touching the feet of Mahendra Singh, Nagendra said, "*Maharaj*, not here. Let's go to that place from where the gate of the palace could be seen clearly and where no one could see us."

Hearing this, Mahendra Singh became serious. He asked, "What is the matter? What do you want?"

"*Maharaj*, I will tell you everything on reaching there," said Nagendra stubbornly.

"OK," said Mahendra Singh and took Nagendra to a secret chamber. From there the gate of the palace could be seen clearly.

"Yes, this is the appropriate place," said Nagendra looking at the gate.

"Now tell me Nagendra," asked Mahendra Singh getting impatient. "Why did you force me to come here?"

"*Maharaj*, finally, the moment has arrived when I can ask for my first reward," said Nagendra Singh and looked at the king. "My first reward is for you to ask the army to get ready. It could get orders to attack at any moment."

Mahendra Singh was stunned to hear this. He said, "Nagendra, you are a brave and responsible soldier. I know that you are not kidding with me, but tell me the matter clearly."

"*Maharaj*, let the appropriate time come. I will tell you everything. But first you give me my first reward," said Nagendra.

"Don't worry. There are four contingents who are always ready to attack. I only have to ring the war bell," said Mahendra Singh pointing towards a bell.

Just then, a man could be seen going towards the gate of the palace. Because of darkness, he could not be recognised. The man was looking here and there.

Seeing him, Mahendra Singh said to Nagendra, "Who is this man? His intentions don't look good. And where are the soldiers?"

"I think they are still not in their senses after the celebration," said Nagendra making faces.

Mahendra Singh got suspicious. He picked up his bow and arrow. Taking the advantage of the darkness, the man had reached the gate and was trying to open it. Seeing this, Mahendra Singh got enraged. Getting ready with his bow and arrow, he said, "I think he is a traitor. Let me ......"

Nagendra Singh stopped the king from shooting his arrow. He said, "Stop *Maharaj*, this is my second reward. I want to accomplish this task."

Mahendra Singh couldn't understand anything. He looked at Nagendra surprisingly and handed

him the bow and the arrow. As soon as the suspected man opened the palatial gate, Nagendra's arrow pierced his back. The very next moment, Nagendra rang the bell.

As soon as the gate was opened, the army of the enemy entered the palace. But the soldiers of Tikamgarh were well prepared. They attacked the intruders with full force. Soon, the enemy army was defeated and the gate was again closed. Taking Nagendra with him, Mahendra reached the gate. The body of the man was lying there. Seeing his face, Mahendra Singh could not believe his eyes. The man was none other than the army chief of Tikamgarh and Nagendra's father Gajendra Singh.

"It means you knew all about this," Mahendra Singh said to Nagendra with tears in his eyes.

"Yes *Maharaj*," said Nagendra and bowed down his head. "I had heard the conversation between my father and the British messenger. I could not believe my ears that because of some wealth, my father could become a traitor. I am ashamed of myself being the son of such a father. I wanted to kill him at that very moment but I wanted to catch him red-handed. Moreover, if I had told you about everything at that moment, you would not have believed me."

"I still am not being able to believe my eyes and ears. Is this a bad dream?" said Mahendra Singh looking at the blood-stained body of his brother. "I had full faith in my brother. He was so close to me. The person whose responsibility was to protect the

kingdom was trying to betray his motherland to the British. This is so shameful."

Nagendra continued, "I was in a fix since a long time. First, I could not think of any reason why my father was doing so. Was it for me? After him, I ought to be looking after everything. But then my soul censured me. I felt that if I accepted his plans, I would not be able to forgive myself throughout my life. For this reason, I made this secret plan, so that no one could suspect me and I could catch the traitor."

Saying so, Nagendra started shedding tears. Mahendra Singh somehow consoled him and said,  "Nagendra, you have done a great job at such a tender age. You have given a big sacrifice, my son. You are a true Rajput and a patriot. I am proud of you."

Nagendra Singh could not control his emotions. He cried very bitterly on the body of his father. But somewhere in the back of his mind, he was proud of himself for being a true son of his motherland.

THE AIM OF NOORJAHAN

It was evening time. The sun was setting down behind the beautiful mountains. Noorjahan was sitting on the terrace of the palace and was enjoying the beauty of nature. Just then, a maid came there and after saluting her, said, "*Malika-e-Alia*, the sun has set. In a few moments, it will be moist. You should not sit under the bare sky. You might fall sick. Let's go inside."

Noorjahan looked at the sky and said while getting up, "Yes, the sun has already set, but *Alampannah* has still not arrived. Where is he strolling at this time of the day?"

"*Malika-e-Alia*, you know Your Majesty is so fond of hunting," the maid reassured Noorjahan. "He doesn't return from the jungle till he gets a good hunt."

"That I know. Don't know what fun he gets by hunting?" Noorjahan murmured walking down the stairs.

"*Malika-e-Alia*, hunting is a symbol of bravery," said the maid. "It is very tough to aim at a running animal. Everyone can not do this."

"How do you know this?" Noorjahan asked the maid.

"My brother is very fond of hunting. He told all this to me," said the maid with a sense of pride.

Noorjahan felt as if the maid was right. She went to her chamber with the thought of hunting in her mind. She thought if even maids and servants knew archery then she should also learn that.

At night, when Jahangir returned from hunting, Noorjahan kept her desire in front of him, "*Alijaan*, is archery a very difficult task?"

"No, not at all," replied Jahangir. "But why are you asking this? Do you want to hunt someone?"

"You are always in a mood of kidding," said Noorjahan shyly. "Actually, I was thinking to learn archery."

"That's great," Jahangir exclaimed. "You should learn archery. I will make all the arrangements

tomorrow."

From the next day, a female soldier started teaching Noorjahan archery. Noorjahan was very confident about herself. Within four-five days, she learnt archery. Now whenever she would get time, she would go to the garden and practise archery.

One day, Noorjahan was strolling on the terrace of the palace with bow in her hand. Just then, a pigeon flew by that side. Noorjahan aimed and shot an arrow at it. Unfortunately, the arrow missed the target and struck a man who was passing by the palace. The arrow hit the man's heart and he died then and there. Seeing this, Noorjahan got frightened. She quietly went to her room and hid the bow and the quiver.

The man who had died was a poor woodcutter. He was returning to his home after cutting wood from the jungle. He had his wife and four little children as his family. When his wife came to know about his death, she started crying bitterly. A neighbour of the woodcutter tried to make the widow understand, "Your husband died by a royal arrow. You should go to the emperor and complain about it. He will surely do justice." Another woman also said the same thing to the woodcutter's wife.

The wife stopped crying. She loaded her husband's body in a carriage and went towards the palace. Emperor Jahangir had got a bell hanged at the gate of the palace. If a person had any problem, he could come to meet him at any time of the day. When the woman reached the palace, it was late night. She rang the bell. Hearing the sound, the emperor asked Noorjahan, "Who could it be at this time?"

Noorjahan's heart started beating faster. 'What if it is the wife of the woodcutter ringing the bell?' she thought. She could not utter even a single word. Jahangir looked at Noorjahan surprisingly and went out to hear the

plaintiff.

On seeing the emperor, the woman started crying loudly. "Lord, please do justice with me. Someone has killed my husband."

"Who are you? And who killed your husband?" asked Jahangir in surprise. "Tell me the entire matter. I promise you that you will get justice."

The woodcutter's wife narrated the entire incident to the emperor, "*Alijaan*, I am a poor woman. My husband used to cut wood from the jungle and we earned our livelihood by selling that wood. Today, when he was returning from the jungle, an arrow came from the side of the palace and killed my husband. I have become a widow now. What will happen to me? What will be the future of my kids?"

"Please be quiet. You will get justice," said the emperor and ordered a soldier, "Go and find out who shot dead the woodcutter. The one who is guilty should be presented before me right now."

On getting the order, the soldier went inside. After some time, he returned with Noorjahan. Seeing Noorjahan, the emperor got angry. He said, "So you made this woman a widow? You will surely get punishment for your negligence."

Emperor Jahangir looked all around. He saw a soldier who was standing with a bow. The emperor took his bow and snapped an arrow from his quiver. Giving it to the woman, he said, "Sister, now you can take revenge from the one who made you widow. Kill this woman's husband right now."

The woodcutter's wife was shocked. She said with folded hands, "No Lord, I can't even think of this. If my husband could get alive by killing you then also I wouldn't have done this. Moreover, Her Majesty didn't do it intentionally. I forgive her."

Seeing the modesty of the poor woman, Noorjahan

got emotional. She fell down at the feet of the woman and cried, "I am very ashamed of my misdeed."

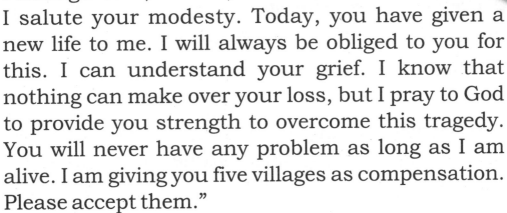

The woodcutter's wife made Noorjahan stand up. Then she said, "You are the queen of this kingdom. Don't make me feel guilty by falling at my feet."

Jahangir said, "Sister, I salute your modesty. Today, you have given a new life to me. I will always be obliged to you for this. I can understand your grief. I know that nothing can make over your loss, but I pray to God to provide you strength to overcome this tragedy. You will never have any problem as long as I am alive. I am giving you five villages as compensation. Please accept them."

On getting the money, the woodcutter's wife heaved a sigh of relief. She said, "I am happy that you are our king. May God give you a blissful life." She bowed to the Emperor and the Queen and then returned to her house with the body of her husband.

When the woodcutter's wife was gone, Emperor Jahangir stared at Noorjahan. There was tears in her eyes. Noorjahan thought, 'From today I will never touch bow and arrow; things that can take one's life.'

WATER BUBBLE

There was a small village in Amritsar. One day an old man came out of his cottage and started preparing his bullock cart. After getting ready, he called out his son, "Son, be fast. We will get late for the city."

"Father, I am coming," came the reply and a 17-18 year old boy stepped out of the cottage.

The boy was holding a lunch box. Keeping that in the carriage, the boy said, "Father, I will drive the cart today."

"Did I ever refuse you?" said the father. Both the father and son rode the carriage and set off for the city. After some time, the carriage stopped in front of a structure. It was a gurudwara. The father tied the bulls to a tree and both of them went inside the gurudwara. Inside, the tenth guru of the Sikhs, Guru Govind Singh was preaching.

The guru was saying, "Brothers, our guru, Tegh Bahadur has been martyred in Delhi. He never compromised with the truth. According to him, our life is like a water bubble. A bubble takes birth in water and ends its life there in. The lifespan of a bubble is very short, but it doesn't regret for it. Why? Because it knows the purpose of its birth and what work it has to perform in its short lifespan."

It was a large congregation. Everyone was quiet and listening to Guruji. Guruji continued, "Our life is also just like a water bubble. But we don't realise this fact of life. The day we will understand this fact, our life will become complete."

The preaching lasted for an hour. When it ended, the father and the son came out of the gurudwara. Both of them were feeling hungry. They sat down under a tree and had their lunch. After that they moved ahead.

On the way, the son asked his father, "Father, what was Guruji saying? How can our life be like a water bubble? A bubble lasts for just a few seconds but our life is so long."

"Don't know son," replied the father. "These are the sayings of great people. We are mere farmers. We will not understand such things."

"But father, since Guruji said it, it must have got some meaning. We should try to understand that."

"Son, if we could understand the preaching of great people, we could also become a preacher. To understand these things, the blessings of God should be with you," said the father.

It had grown very dark. No one could be seen on the road. Suddenly, the boy saw someone walking down the road. Pointing at him, the boy said to his father, "Father, it seems that someone is going to the city. Should we give him a lift in our carriage?"

"Sure son," said the father. The boy called out to that man, "Sir, come and sit down in our carriage. We are also going to the city." The man didn't say anything and

sat down in the carriage. After some time, the boy again asked his father, "Father, Guruji was saying that if we understand the meaning of the bubble then our life will become complete. Is our life at present incomplete?"

"Son, how could I know this? I am an illiterate person. When we will meet Guruji again, you can ask him," said the father.

Hearing this, the stranger sitting in the carriage spoke out, "Soon, you will come to know about this."

Both the father and the son got surprised when they heard this. It was Guruji's voice. The father went near Guruji and said with folded hands, "Guruji, where are you going?"

"Delhi," said Guruji. "Aurangzeb had hung the dead body of Tegh Bahadur at a crossroads. The onlookers throw stones and spit at him. I am going to bring it back."

"But Guruji, this is a very dangerous task.

Please give this responsibility to us. We will do this task at any cost."

But Guruji didn't agree with them. Then the farmer thought of a plan. He said to Guruji, "You have come so far in our carriage. For this, you have to pay the fare."

"Fare," exclaimed Guruji, "But I have nothing to give you."

"Then give us this responsibility as our fare," said the farmer. "We promise you that we will fight till the last drop of blood in our body."

Seeing the determination of the farmer, Guruji had to give the responsibility to him. He gave him his sword and blessed him. The farmer happily moved towards Delhi with his son. The corpse of Guru Teg Bahadur was hung in the middle of a busy road. A foul smell was coming out of the body as

it had been hanging there from many days. People were throwing stones and spitting on the body. Two guards were also positioned there in case of any riot. After examining the entire situation, the father and the son returned to their inn. They decided to complete the work during nighttime. According to the plan, they both reached the spot at midnight. There was no one around the corpse.

The son hurriedly cut the rope with the sword and brought the corpse down. Keeping the corpse down, he said to his father, "Father, let us move out from here quickly before any soldier comes here."

"Son, Amritsar is very far from here," said the father thinking about something. "In a few moments the soldiers will come to know about this and they will start searching for the corpse everywhere. Where will we hide then?"

"Then what should we do," asked the son.

"Son, remember the words of Guruji. This life is like a bubble. Let us complete our work before it ends," said the father. "Do one thing, just separate the head from my torso and hang me in place of Guru Teg Bahadur. People will treat my body as Guruji's body, meanwhile you can reach Amritsar with the body of the divine soul."

"Father!" exclaimed the son. "What are you saying?"

"Son, hurry up. Every moment is precious for us. Before any soldier comes here, just do as I told you," said the father with tears in his eyes.

"No father, I can't do that," the boy cried out.

"Son, please hurry up. We don't have time."

The son looked at his father. Suddenly, he felt as if some divine power entered his body. He at once cut the head of his father. Then he hung the body and moved towards the carriage with Guruji's body.

He kept the body in the carriage and covered it with thatch. Then he set off towards Amritsar. On reaching Amritsar, he handed over the body of Guru Tegh Bahadur to Guru Govind Singh and narrated him the whole incident.

Guru Govind Singh embraced the boy and said, "Son, you have proved that you are a true Sikh. History will never forget you and your father."

Many years passed by. Everyone knew that the one who brought the body of Guru Tegh Bahdur to Amritsar was a young boy of 17 years. But no one knows the name of this brave boy even today.

THE FORT OF RANTHAMBORE

The fort of Ranthambore was surrounded by the army of Alauddin Khilji, the sultan of Delhi. For a long time, the fort was under the siege of the enemy. The soldiers of King Hamir were attentively guarding the fort from the turrets. Whenever the soldiers of the sultan would move ahead they would be attacked with arrows and stones. Having no other option, they would have to step back.

The main reason of this conflict was Alauddin's army chief, Meer Muhammadshah. Muhammadshah had been ousted by Alauddin due to some reasons. Muhammadshah had come to Delhi and took shelter there. When sultan came to know about this, he got angry. He sent a message to Hamir not to give shelter to Muhammadshah, otherwise he would have to face the consequences.

Hamir took it as a challenge. He send a strong reply that he was a true Rajput and it was his duty to protect the one who come under his shelter.

Hearing this, Alauddin Khilji got annoyed. He attacked the fort of Ranthambore with a huge army. The fort of Ranthambore was located amidst high hills and steep valleys. The walls of the fort were so high that they could not be crossed over. Having no other option, Alauddin surrounded the fort.

King Hamir gave the responsibility of protecting each of the four sides of the fort to one general. He was to make sure that no one could forcibly enter the fort. The sultan understood that it was impossible to enter the fort without winning over the four generals. Therefore, he made a plan. He wrote a message on four pieces of cloth and threw them at the four corners of the fort, using arrows. The soldiers handed over the pieces of cloth to their generals. It read 'Why are you being so stubborn? You know that you cannot survive for long in front of us. One day, you are bound to open the gates of the fort. Then you all would be killed by my soldiers. It would be better for you to support us and earn a lot of money'.

On reading the message, two generals named Ratipala and Ranmal. became corrupt. At night, they sent a message to the sultan. Sultan on reading the message became happy. His plan had bore result.

At midnight, Ratipala threw a dead animal in the flowing water of the stream. Because of this the water got polluted. The second general Ranmal hid the grains of the godown. In a few days, there was shortage of food and water inside the fort.

When King Hamir came to know about this, he called an urgent meeting of his generals and ministers and put the situation in front of them.

"*Maharaj*, how long will we remain imprisoned like this in the fort?" said Ratipala. He was eager to get the reward from the sultan. Ranmal also spoke up, "I think that we should open the gates of the fort and attack the army of the sultan."

"No *Maharaj*, it would be a big mistake," protested the

prime minister. "It would be better for us to wait for the right time. It might happen that the enemy may not bear the extreme heat and lift the siege of the fort."

"But *Maharaj*, would it not prove our cowardice?" Ratipala tried to arouse the self-respect of Hamir.

"Moreover *Maharaj*, our provision of food is also running out. The water of the stream has got polluted. Now our only hope rests on the wells in the fort. In such a scenario, how long can we survive on the fort?" asked Ranmal.

Hamir thought for some time and then said, "Now we have only one option left. Open the gates of the fort and attack the enemy. Either we will win the battle or else we will die as martyrs."

The army chief started preparing for the battle. Hamir had decided that if he lost the battle then Alauddin should not get anything from the fort. He ordered his soldiers to dig tunnels and fill them with gunpowder. The guards of the fort were instructed that if the army of Ranthambore seemed to be winning the battle then a red flag will be waved. If the army seemed to be losing, a blue flag will be waved. If the second case happens, they should blow off the fort. In this way, the women and children inside the fort will be spared from being insulted.

At the scheduled time, the gates of the fort were opened and the army of Hamir attacked Alauddin's army. A fierce battle broke out. Everywhere, there were heaps of corpses. The sultan's army was not used to fight in the hilly regions. Soon, they started losing the battle. Seeing this, Ranmal and Ratipala felt as if their plan was going down the drain. They both went near the fort and waved the blue flag. When the guards inside the fort saw the blue flag, they ignited the gunpowder and the whole fort reduced to flames.

When Hamir's army saw this sight, they lost their morale. Alauddin's army took advantage of this situation. They attacked Hamir's army with full vigour. In a few moments, Hamir's army had to face the defeat. All the soldiers of Hamir died. Hamir was now fighting the soldiers of Alauddin all alone. But what could he have done alone? The sultan's army surrounded him from all the sides and killed him mercilessly. Alauddin won the fort of Ranthambore.

Alauddin felt very sad on seeing the condition of the fort. He got emotional. Just then, Ratipala and

Ranmal came to him thinking that they would get huge sum of money as their rewards. On seeing those two traitors, Alauddin shouted, "Everything that happened to the fort of Ranthambore today is because of these two traitors. Thousands of innocent children and women died just because of you."

"But we did it only for you…….," said Ranmal.

"Yes, and for that you will get reward," said the sultan and ordered his soldiers to kill them . "When they couldn't be loyal to their motherland, how can they be loyal to me?"

The soldiers killed Ranmal and Ratipala.Hundreds of years have passed since this incident, but even today you can hear this story from the mouths of people who live there.

THE MARRIAGE PROPOSAL

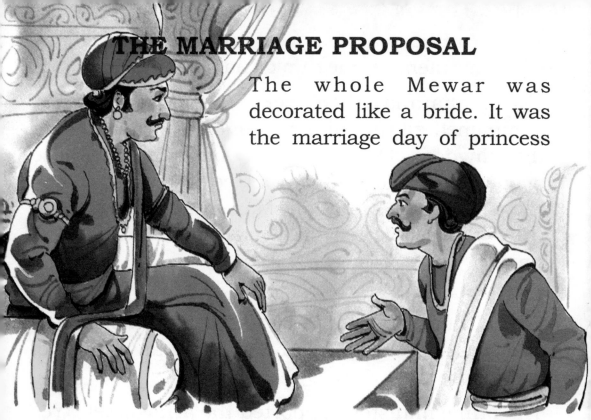

The whole Mewar was decorated like a bride. It was the marriage day of princess Krijna. Not only the royal family, but the whole Mewar was making arrangements for the marriage ceremony. The Maharana of Mewar, Bhim Singh was sitting in his chamber and was guiding his people about the preparations of the marriage. Just then a spy came there and saluted the king. He said, "Maharana, the king of Jaipur Man Singh is preparing his army to launch an attack. He wants to foil the marriage of King Jagat Singh, the would be son-in-law of Mewar."

On hearing the spy, Bhim Singh got surprised, "How is this possible? Just a few days ago, Jagat Singh defeated him."

"Maharana, Sardar Aamir Khan is helping Man Singh in his evil plans."

"Oh, this is bad indeed," said the maharana. Then he

said, "You keep a close watch on the proceedings with your men. Let me think what I should do."

The maharana then sent a messenger and summoned all the ministers and the army chief of the kingdom. On getting the message, all these people assembled in the palace. After describing them the whole situation, Man Singh asked them, "Now you people tell me what should I do at this time?"

First, the army chief spoke, "Maharana, this is a critical time. We should be cautious of Man Singh and get our army ready to face any kind of eventuality."

The prime minister supported the army chief, "Yes Maharana, the army chief has given a good suggestion. We should ask our army to get prepared and also inform the king of Jodhpur Jagat Singh about the development."

"Yes, you are right," said the king. "I hope the marriage procession hasn't set off yet. We should

inform them as soon as possible."

A messenger was immediately sent to Jodhpur. On the other hand, the army was asked to remain on high alert. The subjects of Mewar became worried. On one side, there were arrangements for the marriage and on the other, the preparations for the war.

When the queen came to know about the matter, she got tensed. She said to the king, "Maharaj, I am feeling very frightened."

"There is nothing to be afraid of," said the maharana. "A true Rajput should always be ready for a war. Moreover, Jagat Singh has already defeated Man Singh a few days back. This time, we are also there to help him. We will shed even the last drop of our blood, but will not let any problem overcast on our son-in-law." Saying so, the maharana went out of the chamber. The queen went to the temple located in her chamber and bowed before the goddess. She recalled the day when Princess Krijna's marriage proposal was sent to the king of Jaipur.

When the royal priest reached Jaipur with the

proposal, the king of Jaipur had already died. After him, Man Singh took the reins of the kingdom in his own hands. The royal priest didn't find it right to give the proposal to the new king. Therefore, he returned to Mewar.

When Maharana Bhim Singh heard the whole affair, he supported the step taken by the priest. But now the problem was that who should be sent the marriage proposal. The queen suggested to send the proposal to Jaipur again, but the maharana rejected it, saying that it would be unauspicious now. After a lot of thinking, it was decided to send the proposal to the king of Jodhpur, Jagat Singh.

Jagat Singh happily accepted the marriage proposal. In return, he gave some royal robes and jewellery for the princess.

When King Man Singh came to know about all this, he became annoyed. When the royal priest was

returning from Jodhpur, his soldiers surrounded him and snatched away all the presents. Jagat Singh became furious at this and attacked Jaipur. A fierce battle took place between the two kingdoms. The army of Jagat Singh was large in number as compared to Man Singh's. Soon the army of Man Singh started losing the battle. When Man Singh saw this, he fled away. Jagat Singh chased him, but Man Singh was very lucky to escape him. Meanwhile, Jagat Singh's men gave him the news that some riot had taken place in his kingdom. So, Jagat Singh had to return to Jodhpur.

Man Singh couldn't sleep for many days. He kept planning to take revenge. For this, he shook hands with a Muslim sardar named Aamir Khan. They both planned that when the marriage procession of Jagat Singh would move towards Mewar, they would attack and kill him.

When the spy of Mewar gave this news to Jagat Singh, he flew into a rage. He ordered his army chief to get ready for the war. Jagat Singh rode an elephant and the army marched towards Mewar.

When Princess Krijna came to know about this, she got worried. She thought that because of her, two armies were going to face each other. To win over a princess, thousands of innocent soldiers were going to meet their end. Thousands of families will be ruined. So many women will become widows and children will become orphans. She considered herself responsible for the war.

Princess Krijna thought, 'This should not happen at any cost. The princess of Mewar could not be a murderer. I need to do something so that the war could be avoided.' She put on her thinking cap. Suddenly, she came up with an idea. 'Yes, it is the best idea,' thought she. She was firm in her mind.

The armies of Jaipur and Jodhpur had reached outside the fort of Mewar. On one side, Jagat Singh leading his army in the robe of a groom and on the other side, the combined army of Man Singh and Aamir Khan. The two sides gazed at each other with hatred.

The battle was about to start, when suddenly, the gate of the fort opened. The two armies looked at that direction. A soldier on a horse was riding fast towards them.

Seeing the soldier coming towards the battlefield, Man Singh became happy. He thought that

Maharana Bhim Singh had agreed to give his daughter's hand in marriage to him getting frightened of his huge army. On the other side Aamir Khan, who actually wanted to weaken the strength of the two Rajput kingdoms got tensed to see the soldier. He thought, 'I hope Maharana Bhim Singh hasn't send any peace message for both the kings. Otherwise all my plans would go in vain.'

Maharana Jagat Singh also got confused to see the soldier. He thought, 'I hope Maharanaji hasn't become afraid on seeing the huge army of Man Singh and Aamir Khan. If this has happened, I will destroy Man Singh. Princess Krijna is only mine.'

The soldier came and stood in between the two armies. He shouted, "Stop this war! Princess Krijna has given her sacrifice. She has committed suicide by drinking poison."

The two kings could not believe their ears. They bowed down their heads in shame and returned to their kingdoms.

THE REAL LION

That day, there was a festive mood in the court of Mughal Emperor Aurangzeb. Diwan-e-Aam was crowded with people. Just then, Aurangzeb stepped into the court. After some formal works, the proceedings of the court started.

The *Daroga* said in his manly voice, "Your Majesty, the man-eater of Suratpura region has been caught. I want to present it in the court, if you permit me."

"Permission granted," replied Aurangzeb.

On getting the permission, the officer clapped his hands. The people's eyes stuck at the door. In a few moments, a lion in a cage was brought there. The lion was looking here and there. After that, it gave a loud roar. All the people in the court shivered at the thundering roar.

On hearing the roar, the emperor gave a mild smile. He said, "I have never seen such a strong and huge lion in my life. Who has caught it?"

"Me and my friends," said a man standing near the cage.

"Who are you?" asked the emperor.

"My name is Afzal. I have caught many man-eaters till date."

"Great. You have really done something brave. Take this small gift from me," so saying, Aurangzeb took off a necklace from around his neck and threw it at the hunter. On getting the gift, Afzal became very happy. He thanked the emperor and went away.

All the people present in the court were staring at the lion. The lion had cast a magic spell on the emperor. Aurangzeb suddenly spoke up, "Really, this lion looks extremely ferocious. Tell me, could any of our courtiers have caught this lion?"

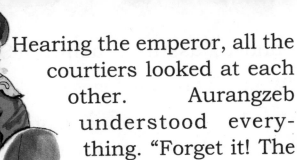

Hearing the emperor, all the courtiers looked at each other. Aurangzeb understood everything. "Forget it! The lion has already been caught," he said. "But can another lion like this be found?"

"Why not, Your Majesty?" said an obsequious courtier. "There are many lions in your court," so saying, he pointed at Yashwant Singh.

Aurangzeb looked at Yashwant Singh and said, "Yashwant, I have heard that Rajputs call themselves lions. Is there any lion who can defeat this lion?"

Yashwant Singh became thoughtful. He felt as if the emperor was challenging him. If he refused to accept the challenge, the fame of the Rajputs would demolish. He said, "I also have a lion, who can defeat this lion."

"Very good," said Aurangzeb. "But the duel will take place empty-handed."

"I agree to it. Rajputs never cheat. My lion will fight with this lion empty-handed," assured Yashwant Singh.

"What if your lion loses?" asked Aurangzeb.

"In that case you can give me death sentence," boasted Yashwant Singh.

"All right. The fight will take place tomorrow. Let me see who wins it," so saying, Aurangzeb dismissed the court.

After reaching his home, Yashwant told the entire matter to his family members. On listening about the fight, his wife said, "What did you do? You want your young son to fight that dangerous lion? I cannot let this happen."

"Do you want my insult in front of everyone in the court?" said Yashwant Singh. "People will say that my blood has rotten. Being a Rajput, I cannot back off from my promise."

"No father, I will not let it happen. I will fulfill your promise," said Prithvi Singh, son of Yashwant Singh. "Your lion will surely defeat the lion of the emperor. This is my promise."

"But son......," his mother wanted to say something.

Prithvi Singh intervened, "No mother, this is the question of the prestige of Rajputs. Bless me so that I can keep the fame of Rajputs high."

Prithvi's mother didn't say anything. Prithvi Singh fell at her feet and said, "Bless me, mother."

"You will win," said the mother and embraced him. She blessed him a thousand times from her heart.

After all she was a mother. She tried a lot to control herself, but some drops of tears came out of her eyes.

The next day, the whole court was crowded with people. People from far and wide had come to Aurangzeb's court to witness a daring and unique display of bravery. When the emperor arrived at the court, Yashwant Singh pointed at his son and said, "Your Majesty, this is my lion. Please make arrangements for the fight between the two lions."

"But he is just a boy," said Aurangzeb looking at Prithvi Singh. "Yashwant Singh, have you gone mad. Why are you throwing your son into the well of death?"

"Only time will tell, who is sending whom into the well of death," said Yashwant Singh with pride. "Just trust him. He is the son of a Rajput."

"OK, let the fight start," ordered the emperor.

In a few moments, the lion was brought in the court. He was imprisoned in a big cage. The hunter opened the door of the cage and pushed Prithvi Singh inside the cage. The lion stared at Prithvi Singh and sat down at a corner. Seeing this, the hunter poked the lion with his spear. The lion got enraged. It gave a loud roar and pounced on Prithvi Singh.

Prithvi Singh was already ready for this. He quickly bent down on his left. The lion got angry at this. It turned back and again attacked Prithvi Singh. This time, Prithvi Singh stopped him by the force of his hands. But because the weight of the lion was much, he lost his balance and fell down. The claws of the lion wounded Prithvi Singh's cheeks and they started bleeding profusely.

The people were watching the fight with gimlet eyes. Every moment they felt as if the fight was going to end, but it continued. On one occasion, even after falling down on the ground, Prithvi Singh didn't lose his courage. He caught hold the jaws of the lion and tore them using all his force.

The lion cried out loudly. There was still enough strength left in the lion. It attacked Prithvi Singh

with its sharp claws. But Prithvi Singh cleverly saved himself from the attack and caught the claws of the lion. The lion tried a lot but could not free itself. Soon, Prithvi Singh ripped the thighs of the lion.

The whole court was stunned to see all this. It was an unbelievable scene. The whole court clapped and shouted with joy looking at the bravery and strength of that young boy.

Yashwant Singh couldn't control his emotions. He ran up to the cage. By then, Prithvi Singh had come out of it. Yashwant Singh kissed his son's forehead and embraced him. He patted Prithvi Singh's back and said, "Son, you have kept my honour and the honour of all the Rajputs. Today you have proved that Rajputs are really lions."

Aurangzeb was not able to believe his eyes. He went up to Prithvi Singh and not caring about his blood-stained clothes, he hugged him tightly.

THE RING THIEF

The court of Fatehpur Sikri was all set. Emperor Akbar was sitting on his throne. Just then, two plaintiffs named Rau Miyan and Rajjan Miyan were presented in the court. Both of them saluted the emperor. The emperor asked the *Daroga*, "What is the matter?"

"Your Majesty, these two people are fighting over an interesting matter," said the officer. "According to Rau Miyan, he had given hundred gold coins to Rajjan Miyan a month ago in his dream."

"In dream!" exclaimed Akbar. "What do you mean?"

"Lord, he is claiming so," said the officer.

When the officer completed his statement, Rau Miyan said, "Lord, actually at that time, Rajjan Miyan was in great need of money. For this reason, I had given him hundred gold coins as a loan. But now he is refusing me to return the money."

"Rajjan Miyan, what do you have to say?" asked the emperor. "Is he telling the truth?"

"Yes Your Majesty," Rajjan replied.

"Then why are you not returning his money?"

"*Alampanaah*, I would have returned the money if I had it," murmured Rajjan.

The emperor became thoughtful. Just then the qazi spoke out, "Lord, this is not a case but a joke."

Just then another officer entered the court. After saluting the king, he said, "Lord, we have caught a ring thief. We have seized a ring from him."

The emperor was already puzzled regarding the previous case. He didn't listen to the officer properly and ordered, "Imprison the thief at once."

Hearing the order, the officer turned back to go. By then the thief himself had appeared in the court. After saluting the emperor, he said, "Your Majesty, the law is deaf and blind. It only sees what is shown to it and hears what is told to it. Therefore, a judge should listen to everything carefully before giving his decision. Otherwise innocent people may suffer."

Hearing the sensible talks of the thief, Emperor Akbar was pleased. He looked at the thief carefully. His face looked familiar to him. He said, "I am very pleased with your words. Who are you? Your face seems familiar to me."

"Lord, I will tell you about my identity later. But if you permit me, I want to help you in solving this case."

Faizi, one of the nine gems in Akbar's court didn't like the thief interfering in the courtly matters. He said, "In which way can you help Your Majesty? Lord, according to me, this is a fake case. These two men should be whipped ten times for wasting the time of the court."

At this, Akbar said, "Faizi, didn't you hear that law is deaf and blind. That's why it is important to take the advice of every people before giving decision on any issue." Then he gave permission to the thief to give his advice.

"Thank you Your Majesty," said the thief humbly. "The faith you have shown in me, I will not let it go in vain. The case of these two men is very simple. Please ask one of your attendants to bring a mirror and a hundred gold coins. I will settle this matter just now."

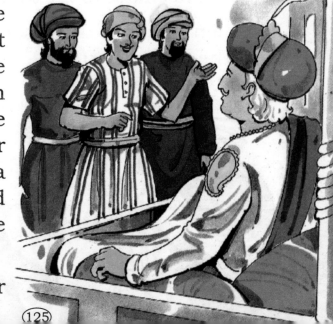

Emperor Akbar

signalled an attendant and soon a mirror and a hundred gold coins were brought in the court. The thief then made the mirror stand against a wall and kept the coins in front of it. After that, he said to Rau, "Rau Mian, can you see the reflection of the coins in the mirror?"

"Yes, I can see," said Rau.

The thief further said, "Now you can take the hundred coins from the mirror."

"How is this possible?" Rau got confused.

"If you cannot take the coins seeing their reflection in the mirror then how can you give coins to someone in a dream, as a dream is also like a reflection," concluded the thief.

Seeing the judgement of the thief, Akbar was stunned. He said, "Your intelligence is really praiseworthy. What a decision you have made! This is your reward." Saying so, Akbar gave away his costly necklace to the thief.

Just then Akbar recalled something. He said, "Are you the woodcutter whom I had met in the

Kalpi jungle?"

"Yes Your Majesty, you have guessed it right," said the thief taking the necklace. "I am that woodcutter, Mahesh."

Emperor Akbar recalled the incident that had happened a few months ago during the summer. It was a very hot day. The emperor had gone for hunting with Atagbegh and Kalyanmal. Chasing a lion, Akbar had reached the densest part of the jungle. At last, he succeeded in killing the lion. It was noon and the sun was blazing just overhead. Akbar and his companions were feeling very hungry and thirsty. But there was no source of food or water.

Just then Akbar heard some noise. He felt as if someone was cutting wood. Akbar and his companions moved towards the direction of the noise. After covering some distance, they saw a youth who was cutting wood. Seeing him, Kalyanmal shouted, "O boy, do you have some water?"

The name of the youth was Mahesh. He didn't reply. Atagbegh felt very angry. He stared at the boy and shouted again, "Can't you listen, we are asking for water?"

At this Mahesh replied, "It is very surprising. You are asking for water and that too so arrogantly. I think you are from a good family but don't you know that you should be polite while requesting for something?"

Hearing Mahesh, Atagbegh and Kalyanmal took out their swords. Akbar stopped them and said, "Please forgive them, they are ignorant. Actually, we came to the jungle for hunting. We are now feeling very hungry and thirsty. Please if you could provide us with some water."

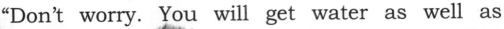

"Don't worry. You will get water as well as something to eat. But first let me tell you something. It is dangerous to have a bad company. You should think deeply about such companions."

Hearing Mahesh, Atagbegh and Kalyanmal got furious but Akbar laughed. Mahesh then handed over his lunch to Akbar.

"What's this? Dry *chapati* and chilli," Kalyanmal said astonishingly. Akbar stared at him. Kalyanmal became quiet. Akbar first drank some water and then started eating the *chapatis* and chilli with relish. Atagbegh and Kalyanmal were surprised.

After eating to his fill, Akbar said to Mahesh, "It was great. I never ate such a delicious meal. But what will you eat now as I have eaten your lunch?"

"It is a virtue to give food to the hungry and water to the thirsty. Moreover, my house is nearby. When I'll feel hungry, I will go to my house and eat," said Mahesh.

"Oh, I forgot to ask your name," said Akbar. "You seem to be an intelligent man. Why are you cutting wood?"

"My name is Mahesh," replied the woodcutter. "I live nearby with my uncle

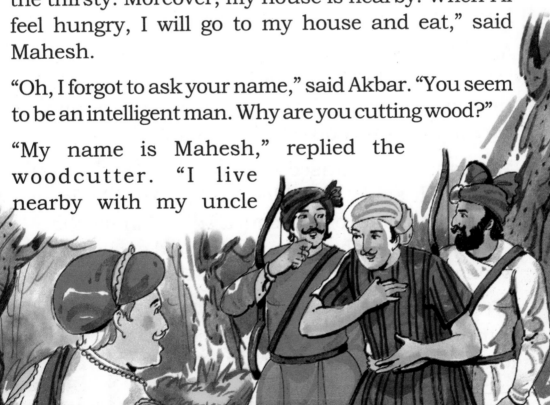

and aunt. I have studied in Kashi Vidyapeeth."

Hearing Mahesh, Akbar was very happy. He said, "That's nice. Can you solve a riddle for me?"

"Ask, I will try my level best."

Akbar asked, "Could there be a person who has the qualities of a saint, a cook and a water-bearer?"

"The answer is, an illiterate brahmin," replied Mahesh. "Because a brahmin is respected right from his childhood. But if he fails to study then he has to work as a cook or a water-bearer."

Akbar felt very happy. Giving him his ring, he said, "My name is Jalaluddin Akbar. I am giving you this ring as a reward. You are an able brahmin. A person like you should be in my court."

Mahesh was surprised to know the identity of the person. He said with folded hands, "Your Majesty, I will surely come to your court. I didn't know that I was talking to the emperor. If I said something wrong, please forgive me."

After returning from hunting, Akbar forgot Mahesh as he got busy with his courtly affairs. And today, the same Mahesh was standing in

front of him as a thief.

Emperor Akbar asked Mahesh, "Mahesh, is this the same ring which I had given to you as a reward?"

"Yes Your Majesty," replied Mahesh.

On hearing the answer, Akbar scolded the officer and asked him to seek forgiveness from Mahesh. Mahesh had already told the officer that Emperor Akbar had given him the ring, but the officer didn't trust him and took him as a thief. The officer sought forgiveness from Mahesh and went away.

"Mahesh, by solving the case of the gold coins, you have once again given the example of your intelligence. From today, you will be called Birbal and will be one of the gems of my court."

"Thanks to you My Lord. I will try to live up to your expectations," said Birbal, Mahesh's new name.

After that, Birbal became one of the nine gems of Akbar's court. He went on to solve the most difficult cases in minutes. He was full of wit and intelligence. People remember him even today.

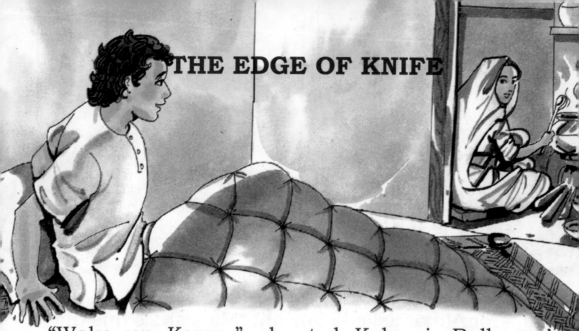

THE EDGE OF KNIFE

"Wake up Karan," shouted Kalyani, Balkaran's mother from the kitchen. Covering a dish full of *jalebis,* she again called out to Balkaran, "Son, wake up. Go to Sujan's house and bring the milk."

"Milk," exclaimed Balkaran. "Mother, what will you do with the milk so early in the morning? I will fetch the milk later."

"Son, I have to cook *kheer.* Go and bring the milk just now," said Kalyani

Hearing the name of *kheer,* Balkaran sat up on his bed. "*Kheer!* What for, mother?"

"Did you forget? Today it is your birthday dear," replied his mother, "that's why…….."

Balkaran didn't wait for his mother to complete her sentence. He was excited about his birthday. He got up from his bed and went into the kitchen. His mother continued, "Look, I have made so many dishes for you. Now go and bring the milk, then I'll make *kheer.*"

"But mother, where is my knife?" asked Balkaran.

"It must be in your bed," replied his mother.

Balkaran ran to his room, moved his pillow and saw the knife lying there. He picked it up and started sharpening it. His mother asked, "Why do you sharpen your knife everyday?"

"Mother, this is my father's memento," was the reply of Balkaran. "He had asked me to keep this knife with me always. It can help me at any difficult time."

After that, Balkaran took a bowl and set off for Sujan's house, which was nearby. On the way, he saw some men running helter-skelter and shouting. Balkaran felt as if something was wrong. He checked his pocket. The knife was intact there. He thought, 'I have my knife with me. I should not get afraid.'

Just then, he thought of his mother, 'But mother is alone at home. I should reach home soon with the milk.' Thinking this, he started walking briskly.

On the other hand, Kalyani got afraid on hearing the noises coming from the street. She came out to see

what was happening. People were running helter-skelter. They were shouting, "Run, run! Taimur's army has arrived."

Kalyani got frightened, 'O my Karan, what should I do? This Turk is such a tyrant..... My son.....!' Kalyani was thinking all this when her neighbour came out of his house with his son. He said to Kalyani, "Sister, run quickly. Taimur's army is approaching our village, destroying everything on its way."

"How could I go *Bhaiya*?" Kalyani cried. "Karan has gone to Sujan's house to bring milk."

"Sister, there is not much time. Balkaran is a sensible boy. He can take care of himself," so saying, the neighbour ran towards the fields with his family. Kalyani was in a fix. Her motherhood was stopping her from taking any step. Kalyani ran and hid herself in the basement.

On the other side, when Balkaran reached Sujan's house, he saw that the place was desolated. Some buckets were lying on the floor and the milk was scattered everywhere.

"Oh, how did the milk scatter here?" Balkaran murmured. He called out to Sujan, "Sujan uncle, I want some milk. Mother is preparing *kheer* for me."

Balkaran kept waiting but he got no response. 'I think Sujan uncle has also ran away like those people. I should reach home as soon as possible,' thinking this, Balkaran took some milk and set off for his home.

In a few moments, Taimur's army entered the village with shining swords in their hands. They straight away went to Kalyani's house. Smelling the sweets, one of the soldiers went to the kitchen. When he removed the covers from the dishes, he saw so many types of sweets. He exclaimed, "Look, so many sweets are waiting for us." The other soldiers were throwing away the belongings of the house in

search of jewellery and money. Hearing the name of sweets, they ran to the kitchen. They fell upon the sweets like hungry lions.

Just then, Taimur entered the cottage of Kalyani. When he saw his men eating sweets, he roared, "Have you come here for looting or to eat sweets?"

The soldiers trembled on hearing the voice of Taimur. They stood up from their places. Just then, Balkaran entered the house, "Mother, I have brought the milk."

Seeing the soldiers, Balkaran shouted, "Who are you and what are you doing in my house?"

"Shut up, you kid!" Taimur roared. "Give this milk to me. I am feeling very thirsty."

"I can't give this milk to anyone," said Balkaran bravely. "My mother is going to cook *kheer* for me with this milk."

Taimur snatched the pot from Balkaran's hands

and started drinking the milk. Balkaran hurriedly picked up Taimur's sword which Taimur had kept aside and warned him, "Don't dare to drink my milk else I will kill you."

At this, Taimur laughed and said, "Return my sword. You are very small for this." Then Taimur moved forward and snatched the sword from Balkaran. Suddenly, Balkaran remembered his knife. He took it out from his pocket and showing it to Taimur, shouted, "What if you snatched the sword? I have a knife. I will fight with it."

"You are the first person to talk to Taimur so courageously," said Taimur. "What is your name?"

"Balkaran," Balkaran gave the reply.

"I am very pleased to see your bravery and courage. You can wish for anything you want," said Taimur.

Balkaran was worried about his mother. He said to Taimur, "Where is my mother?"

"I don't know, little warrior," Taimur replied. "But I can assure you that my men have not killed any person of this village. She might be hiding somewhere."

"Are you telling the truth?" asked Balkaran.

"Yes, I don't lie. The whole world knows this," said Taimur pampering little Balkaran.

Balkaran said, "Just a moment ago, you said that you will give me anything I wish for."

"Yes, I did promise," Taimur said.

"Then leave my village at once."

"OK, as you wish," said Taimur giving a mild smile. Taimur then left the village with his men. Kalyani came out of the basement on hearing the noises.

"Mother, Taimur drank all the milk," said Balkaran innocently.

"It's OK," said his mother. "You have done a great job by saving your village from the hands of Taimur."

Balkaran's face glowed up with pride. His mother embraced and kissed him.

THE BEGUM OF AWADH

The policy of 'Divide and Rule' of the British was proving very effective. Because of this policy, they were able to bring one Indian kingdom after another under their rule. On February 6, 1856, the British issued a proclamation that Awadh should be included in the British Empire. This made the whole kingdom very worried and tensed.

The health of Nawab Wajid Ali Shah was not well. He was not in a condition to deal with the strong British. Therefore, he decided to surrender before them. But his wife, Begum Hazrat Mahal didn't agree to this. She swear on the name of her son Mirza Birjis that she will fight the British till her last breath.

She called the soldiers and addressed them, "Friends, Awadh is our motherland. We will die but never give our

kingdom to the British." The words of the Begum proved very effective. Soon, a large army got ready to fight with the British.

To give support to the queen, every person of the kingdom came forward. Everywhere the praises of the begum could be heard. Hazrat Mahal was leading a strong rebellious force.

This army attacked the British with full force. But the British were already prepared. They stopped the army at Chinhat village. A fierce battle was fought between the two armies. Sir Henry Lawrence was leading the British force. He faced the Awadh army with bravery, but the natives were very difficult to be defeated. When Lawrence saw his army retreating, he stepped back. The British moved out of Lucknow, the capital of Awadh. Now the people of Awadh had the rein of Lucknow in their hands.

After winning Lucknow, Begum Hazrat Mahal was chosen as the ruler of Awadh. But the begum refused to accept the position. She instead appointed Mirza Warjis as the ruler of Awadh.

Within a few days, the begum captured the hearts of the people of Awadh through her ruling capabilities and administration. She would daily roam in the streets of Awadh and ask the people about their problems. She tried her level best to eradicate those problems.

Seeing all this, the people of Awadh were very happy. No other ruler had been so famous in Awadh as Begum Hazrat Mahal.

After losing Awadh, the British formulated another strategy. They collected their forces and again on February 1858, attacked Awadh. Begum Hazrat Mahal and her army gave a good reply to the British. But now the size of her army was very less than that of the British. They started retreating at the face of the roaring British canons.

When Begum saw her army retreating, she acted very cleverly. With some of her trusted soldiers, she ran away from there and took shelter in the fort of Bundi that was located in the Bahrich district. There she started assembling her army again.

The British commander was very well aware of the popularity of Hazrat Mahal. He thought that untill she was caught, he could not take rest. It would be better if she shook hands with him. Therefore, he sent a proposal of peace to Begum. In the proposal it was suggested that the British Government will overlook all of her atrocities. It would also look after her son's education and will provide her pension.

But that woman of self-respect refused to bow

before the British. In her reply she said that she will lay down her life but will not lose her self-respect and the trust of her people.

Hearing this, the British commander got annoyed. He attacked the fort of Bundi with a large army. Hazrat Mahal gave a solid response to the attack. Soon, there could be seen thousands of corpses.

Begum fought very bravely in the battle, but some of her trusted soldiers betrayed her. They got united with the British when the later bribed them with Jagirs. The strength of the army of Hazrat Mahal was already very weak. Soon, the army of Begum started retreating.

Hazrat Mahal's army chief didn't take much time to understand the situation. He said to Begum, "Your Majesty, the British army is huge and powerful. Our

army cannot face them for a long time. Our defeat is destined. You should leave this place with some trusted soldiers."

"No, I can not leave my soldiers like this," shouted Begum. "I will fight till my last breath."

"Please accept my request. Just think about Mirza Warjis,"

said the army chief.

"To continue the freedom struggle it is very important for both of you to stay alive. This time the situation is not in our favour. You should understand this. Take Mirza Warjis with you and leave for Nepal. He will surely give you support," the army chief pleaded.

Begum could not say anything. With her son, she went to the king of Nepal. Hazrat Mahal never forgot this defeat. She was broken because of the betrayal of her trusted men. After the Revolt of 1857, she was totally broken. After that, neither the king of Nepal could support her nor she could assemble her army.

For the rest of her life, she lived like a normal human being. In her journey, her son Mirza Warjis was always with her. At last, one day the story of this great woman ended. She died and left behind her remembrances in this world. Her bravery and administrative powers are still discussed not only in the books but also by the people of Awadh. Even today, when people of Awadh talk about Begum Hazrat Mahal, they feel proud.